ERCH
in
URCHINAGE

ERCH in URCHINAGE

Being
*Stories and Notes about
the Town of Inverness from
1918 to 1939*

By
M. DICK

Illustrated by
C. ARTHUR

ALBYN PRESS
EDINBURGH

© M. Dick 1985

Printed in Great Britain by
Whitstable Litho Ltd., Whitstable, Kent
and published by
ALBYN PRESS
(Charles Skilton Publishing Group)
29 Forth Street
Edinburgh 1

ISBN 0284 98702 6

PREFACE

DO YOU chuckle when reminded of the interesting, stupid or exciting events you experienced in those years between earliest recall and the prison-house of higher learning? If so, you may enjoy reading on, wherever you spent your own Urchinage.

The following tales endeavour to recapture the flavour of activities in Inverness in the '20s and '30s, as enjoyed and suffered by the urchins of the town, who were probably not dissimilar to the urchins of any other small town or village.

I hope they may also evoke happy memories for older Invernessians, nostalgia for the exiled, interest for the present-day townspeople, and prove a pleasing read for all who yearn to reverse the clock.

The stories told are submitted as fiction, as are most of the characters. Lest there be any doubt, I have added an index of those real life personalities who have contributed by their inclusion to the overall picture.

I record my sincere thanks to my boyhood friend C. Arthur, who has so fluently represented the mood in his illustrations.

CONTENTS

First Steps

THE OLD MAN was reading aloud from the local paper, seated on his rocking chair, under the mild hiss of the gas wall bracket. November, and little natural light. Cinders glowed and spat sweetly in the "Registered Grate". It was clearly "Registered," for was not the word and its very own number cast with the metal for all to see, important like? Fire was in the centre, oven to left, and water boiler to right. A black cat with white locket lay sleeping on the scrimp carpet before the fire. Wilting aspidistra centred before the window clad in the conventional lace curtains of the age. Homewood table with two hinged extension flaps in the middle of the room, and against the wall opposite the fire, a bureau (burroo), chest of drawers below, writing desk above, containing numerous fascinating compartments. On top again bookcase, glass fronted – Scott, Dickens, Neil Munro, The Brahan Seer, dictionary, Bible.

The Old Man, in his fifties, but the boss and the master of the house. He bore his title with firmness and gentle modesty. The twinkle was seldom from his bespectacled eye.

"Theatre closed this week. Railway did not deliver the costumes. Robin Hood in the Music Hall. Better watch the gas too. Says here 'Gas pressure reduced owing to shortage of labour and inferior coal.'"

He looked at the gas light.

"Thought the mantle was about done."

Comely Jean, a good ten years his junior, spurtle in hand, gave her wifely acknowledgement of these monosyllabic observations through the open door of the scullery adjoining.

9

This adult conversation was over the head of Erch, all of three years old, trying with a piece of string to interest the sleeping cat in a bit of play. Charles, after Edward Stuart, no more than twisted his whiskers. Not interested.

Charles, in fact, had had a very rough morning. He had stalked a sparrow through the back fence, and into the territory of Nancy, the big black and grey striped bully of a tabby, and enemy of all cats in the street. A great squawking and arching of backs ensued, before Nancy moved in for the kill, drawing blood from Charles' nose and right ear. Charles beat a speedy tactical retreat, tail between legs, and reported home for sympathy. Erch, too, feared Nancy. He had seen how she ruled all the neighbourhood cats, and heard her endless squawks by night as she challenged intruders.

Erch, disgusted by Charles' non-co-operation, got to his feet and approached the door to the lobby and the outside world. He could just reach the slippery brass knob, but had never been able to turn it. This time, in sticky hands, it did not resist. At the turn of the stair, above to his right, the big Edinburgh-made grandfather clock, ticked in Presbyterian solemnity as always, be the family awake or asleep, marking the hours on its tinny bell. The majesty of it gave an air of confidence, endurance, and life to the scene. Every Sunday morning after breakfast the winding ceremony took place. The wooden door which hid the weights and pendulum, and the glass door protecting the face were opened. The big Z shaped winder was inserted to wind up the heavy weights controlling the timing and the striking. Sometimes the Old Man lifted Erch up to perform the winding, helping him with the key, for it was a heavy lift. Always the grandfather was five minutes fast, set by the time ball which fell above Fraser, Ferguson and Macbean's door on Union Street at 1 p.m. on week days. The Old Man checked his watch weekly by the ball, and transferred the time to the grandfather, and the smaller pendulum wall clock in his bedroom.

Erch turned left, his back to the grandfather, and travelled down the highly polished lino, maintaining balance with difficulty. The big front door was ajar. He swung it wide, and carefully stepped down to the "gate", an area represented by four Caithness flags, and reached the cast iron gate, the final barrier. Closed. He stuck his head through the spars, for there was life beyond.

The street was thronged with people, young and old, laughing, shouting, singing, animated, excited, almost delirious. One or two Union Flags poked from the windows opposite. Wonder registered on every feature of the chubby face. This was better than playing with Charlie. Ha'penny Jock from number three, not all there, brought out his melodian and struck up a tuneless Tipperary. Everybody, but everybody hollered the words. Hardly had this finished when a great procession of laughing, shouting youths marched up the street four deep, all in working clothes, and bonnets, like the piper who led them. The Black Squad from the railway. They had a rousing reception, but not more so than the local pipe band, mostly old men resplendent in Highland rig, which followed soon after, or the smart silver band of the American Army.

The happy scene penetrated the consciousness to register as Erch's earliest memory.

The Kaiser's war was over.

That night Erch was washed as usual, face and neck, and arms and knees in the basin in front of the fire, and the Old Man carried him "coal bag" fashion on his back, upstairs to the single bedroom. "Turn y'r haydee t' th' waal boy, an' go t' sleep." Erch turned to the wall and was tucked in. The Old Man patted him on the head, and left the door slightly ajar so that the gaslight on the landing could dispel the darkness a little, and give comfort.

The Old Man was gone for a long, long time when Erch heard a scraping at the window. He turned on his back and saw the silhouette of Nancy stalking him as she did Charles, stealthy, silent, slowly moving towards him, from the window sill, over the dressing table, over the end of the bed, up the bed towards his face. Erch was petrified with fear. He saw the teeth parted, and the venom shining in the eyes. The cat eased back on her haunches for the strike, and slowly lifted a paw. Erch put up an arm to protect his face

11

just as the strike was made. He felt the sharp pain in his arm as the claws sunk in. The cat gloated in her mastery over her prey.

Erch began to yell with all the power in his lungs.

"Help! Help! Help!"

Jean came dashing up the stairs, and took him in her arms, waking him from his nightmare, a dream which was destined to recur until Nancy was reported killed by a wee Scots Terrier whom she tackled and found just too much for her.

The Street

THE STREET, surfaced in rolled rubble, seventy yards long, which was to be the horizon for some time to come, comprised circa 1890 stone built, terraced, slated houses on both sides. All were let to tenants. There was no local authority housing. Between the years 1880 and 1910 there was a burst of private domestic building for letting, soon to be killed by the Rent Acts, an example of well meant legislation which misfired. Stone came from Tarradale Quarry in horse drawn carts, and was cut with cold chisel and mallet by the mason. Hundreds of houses were built between Old Edinburgh Road and Eastgate, between Telford Street/Kenneth Street and Fairfield Road, between Tomnahurich Street/Glenurquhart Road and the river, and in the Farraline Park area. Slates came from Ballachulish via the canal, kitchen and bathroom fittings, ironwork and drainpipes from the Glasgow region by rail. Such building ceased by 1920 when bricks superseded stone. The Town Council took over and erected 500 houses by 1928, and by 1938, 2,500. Between 1820 and 1910 the population jumped from 12,000 to 22,000.

Turning again to Erch's street, each house boasted a parlour, kitchen-cum-livingroom, two and a half bedrooms, and toilet. Erch and his immediate neighbour had a bathroom. No other houses had. The pattern was broken at the foot on one side, where there was a three storey tenement building. No front window was without its lace or pseudo lace curtains, and roller blinds of yellow, oiled cloth. All windows were sash type, top and bottom halves designed to open by sliding up or down. Each house had a strip of ground in front five feet deep, enclosed by a dwarf stone wall surmounted by vertical cast iron spars, each topped with an elaborate cast arrowhead, and there was a gate conforming in design.

First life in the street of a morning was represented by Billy the Baker's boy, undersized at the age of ten, dressed poorly but conventionally – boots, stockings, shorts, jersey. He held his big square basket in the crook of his right arm, and gave out a mournful cry of "Rolls." As he had a lisp, it came out as "Tholls." This meant, warm from the oven, Mirtle's rolls, soft biscuits, butteries, and glazed scones. The softies had a middle dimple, and were best sellers. Poor Billy always looked tired, unwashed, and unhappy.

He was followed by the "scaffies," known today as "cleansing operatives." They had a horse drawn high-sided cart, open on top to the four winds. If one of these winds chose to blow, it lifted the loose papers and scattered them with the customary caprice of nature. The "bins" laid out at the door fronts for their attention might be old oil drums, wooden or cardboard boxes, and in exceptional cases to exhibit great wealth or greater hygiene, a purpose built "bucket" with lid.

Malkie the Milkman, made a theatrical entrance. To emphasise his horsey associations, he wore black boots, black leggings, khaki breeches, old tweed jacket, and bonnet. The neck, like all the street traders and artisans, was innocent of collar and tie, but the shirt was secured at the neck by a stud. Malkie, horse at the trot from the foot of the street, two large milk churns rattling on the two wheeled trap, played his pea whistle in cupped hand to vary the pitch, his tongue for a trill, emitting a sharp "come and get it" tune. Erch watched, fascinated, as Malkie served out the milk, via his pint and half pint measures to the cans of all the wifies in the street. Milk bottles were awaiting invention. The liquid frothed pleasantly from the brass taps on the churns, and the penny ha'penny a pint went into the leather shoulder bag. Nothing could be more desirable than to be a milkman.

For the wifies, a visit to Malkie at the door was a chance for a klaik. If there were enemies in the street, you could watch through the parlour windows, see who was at Malkie's, and plan your visit accordingly.

When ahead of time on his rounds, Malkie would occasionally give a favoured boy a scud on his cart, standing on the step like himself, looking through the churns and over the nag's posterior. What could be more heavenly, with all the jealous eyes of your mates upon you?

After Malkie, the way was clear for Hugh the Post, the King of the News, and no time wasted in the telling. Swift of foot, though slightly crippled by a war. ''Post, post. Sojers no' getteen un th' pichers cos of the flu. Th' pond's bayreen, an' Lloye George is baak.'' The headlines were given out in strict order of precedence. It was most important to all the boys to know when Loch na Sanais (corrupted to Shaaneesh) was ''bayreen.'' Hugh, himself a graceful skater, even with his gammie hoof, would be on the pond hot foot from his round.

Colin Quail, his nag pulling up to twenty bags of coal in a flat lorry, called a monotonous ''Quail'', which the street in general believed to be the Gaelic for coal. His competitor Peter, had a more cheerful ''Coal, Coal, Col'', while Donallie had ''Fy-er-wudd.''

Stewart the Fish, with his horse float, called ''Hayreen, fraysh hayreen, fraysh hareen, hayra, hayra hayreen, fraysh hayreen.'' Tocher, his opposition – ''Haddies, fraysh haddies, fraysh haddies, had, had, haddies, fraysh haddies.'' These two wore their bonnets so far over their right ears, it was a mystery how they stayed on. The bonnet tilt was the insignia of the fishman. Maggie, from far away Nairn, seventy if a day, back creeled, fisherwoman's rig, with ''Speldeens, fraysh speldeens,'' the sweetest of smoked haddies.

If you wanted tatties, turnips or cabbages, you listened for a hand bell, and would buy from Mutch, boots still caked with the good earth of his plot where he had been digging ahead of the sun and of the sleepy town.

By mid-day the stage was cleared for Frank, old man, old coat, old bonnet, old boots, leaning on the shafts of a laden hurley. He took rags and paid in money or in kind. ''Any ol'

15

"Spare a Penny"

rags, bones, bo'les." First variation – "Any ol' rags, bones, bo'les get munny or dushes f'r th'm." Second variation – "Any ol' rags, bones, bo'les, get munny or dushes f'r th'm. Rabbutt skins." Surname unknown, Frank was the favourite of the urchins for sometimes his reward for rags could be a balloon, or for a good load, a canary, on a string, on a stick, with a tail that twirled in the wind.

Beggars were daily. "Spare a penny Missus. Gie's a piece, Missus." Among them the tinkers who no longer tinked. Theirs was a straight begging job – old clothes or a penny. They knew it was nonsense to ask for more than a penny in the street, and if the demand was for a piece, they were seldom turned away.

The more honest pedlars had buttons, reels, or "purns" of thread, needles or matches. And there was Old Moore's Almanack, a must in every house, sold on the doorstep by entrepreneurs. It foretold what was to happen in the coming year, and it was sometimes right. The law of averages applied.

The music makers were pipers, fiddlers, trumpeters, and there were those with squeeze boxes and mouth organs. Sometimes a tin whistle or spoons. There was one barrel organ.

The singers were mostly sad. "Rock of Ages," was an ancient with an ancient wife to do the collecting, so that his mournful rendering would not be interrupted by a thankyou. His offering went: –

"Rock of Ages cleft for me (aside), much dud y' get? Put utt un m' pocketee."

They walked the middle of the street before parking problems were invented.

The primary school children from the Big School and the Wee School round the corner made their way to and fro. On Fridays the wifies of the street set off to town in the early afternoon, and returned late, weary and laden, from the Co-op, and Luptons.

Ackie, a ten year old, was in the kindler trade with his "Bun-dels, penny bun-dels. Please tek a bun-del missus. Ef yull no tek a bun-del ah'll no hev a bed fur th' nite." It is

FOOTBALL TIMES

doubtful if this statement was true, but all is fair in love and war, and business is war. His "bun-del" was quite a good buy and he usually disposed of the whole stock contained in his "bogie." This vehicle, so popular with and beloved of boys, was a home-made wooden box, two foot six inches square, on pram wheels, and with two shafts. Ackie's sales' experience bore fruit. Leaving school at fourteen he became a "bowsher" for a grocer, then a counter hand. With a keen eye to his future he found work in a large multiple store, and ended up a city manager. Not bad for the youngest of a very large family living in slum property, in poverty, with a drunk for a father.

On Saturday evenings the newsboys queued at the Highland News Office in Hamilton Street, awaiting the production of the evening edition – the *Football Times* – which contained a whole page of results and reports. This was delayed in the office until the results and the reports of the local games had arrived. At 6 p.m., with the print still wet, the boys burst on the streets. "Footboll Times." "Fitba 'imes." "Imes." The paper was bought for football interest alone. There were no pools.

As darkness fell the lampie with his big pole and incredible walking pace put spark to the gas lights. The lampies also served in the fire brigade and were accustomed to rushing about. If they failed to light the street lamps it meant they had more important business at a fire.

On Sunday, silence. The Kirk alone was licensed to utter. "Ding, ding, ding." "Ding-dong, ding-dong." "Dong, dong." The heavy stuff, mindful of their little brothers, gave the wee fellows a good start before coming in with their "Crash, bang, Wallop."

The house doors opened almost furtively. The family paraded all dressed up, the bairns uncomfortable and unusually clean, sheepish, with their wee black books. The Papes, the Pisces, the F.P.'s, the Frees, the U.F., the Established, the Baptists, the Jehovahs and the Ebenezers all came out to face the minister or the priest, and prepare for one more week of discord. On week days they were quite good friends, at least tolerating each other. But on Sundays, each member of each sect looked with pity on each member of each other sect, for each member of each sect knew that his sect alone was the chosen, and each member of each other sect must surely have beheld the serpent.

Scenes like these were for Erch and his mates, nourishment and norm.

Head Case

THE OLD MAN knocked his pipe carefully into the embers of the cinder fire.

"Provost Macdonald suggested that as a memorial to the men of Inverness who fell in the war, a large hall should be built in Inverness. The town hall was too small. There could be shops underneath which would pay for the upkeep. There are other halls in the town, but they are owned by private parties."

The halls referred to as being owned by private parties were the Music Hall on Union Street, and the Theatre Royal on Bank Street. Both were losing money. The Music Hall, owned by a private company, was purchased and used by the Wesleyan Methodist Church from 1922, and was burnt to the ground around 1960. The theatre, owned by Miss Graham-Falcon, was burnt to the ground in March 1931, and in the flames the great Will Fyffe lost all his props.

Erch had no desire to be a dramatic artist, apart from the child's inevitable desire to occupy the centre stage in his own small circle.

He was at the gate, firmly closed to prevent his escape to the street. The nose was poked between the spars the better to view the scene. Jim Hogg was home to visit his parents. He came all the way from distant Patagonia, where he was herding sheep and was wealthy. Jim had bought a Model T Ford with a folding roof that was a sensation in the street. Erch was waiting to see the mechanical wonder move. Jim came from his parents' house, the centre of many admiring eyes. He was both modest and kind.

"You, you, you, and you get in."

Four small boys clambered into the car to enjoy their very first experience of motoring.

21

A small knot of people of all ages gathered to view the phenomenon, as always did when some melodrama was promised. The passengers waved furiously, each anxious that his position of preferment be noticed by lesser beings in the role of spectators. One-upmanship was no stranger to this street. Jim was not unaware he was playing the major part in the action. All the boys were made to sit and pledged not to move, the instructions were reinforced by a raised fist, the import of which was gainsaid by his smile. He jumped into the driving seat and made meticulous adjustments to various levers and switches, and alighted again, holding the starting handle. He wound the thing up at the front, and shortly after he had broken sweat, the engine fired, and was galvanised into life. The contraption rattled noisily but merrily. Not without pride, Jim took the wheel and commenced a triumphant drive round the block.

Craning to watch this miracle disappear into the middle distance, Erch's head slipped right through the cast iron spars of the gate. The ears, quite substantial, functioned as barbs of a fish hook do, and prevented retraction. This was good cause for a howl, and a howl was set up. The spectators turned their attention to this new curiosity. Some were sympathetic, some derisive, but to all it was an interesting diversion. Jean came rushing from the house to find the cause of the commotion. Try as she would, she could not dislodge the head from the gate.

Andrew the Blacksmith from next door, ambled up the street with leisurely step, as he had been doing for the past thirty years. He took in the scene at a glance. He looked around the assembled kids, and picked out one of the biggest, Callum, fully ten years.

"Callum, down to the smiddy and ask Willie for a hacksaw."

Callum departed at a trot.

"Missus, get me some butter."

Jean retreated into the house and returned with a small butter dish. Andrew clarted the ears and the side of the head with butter. Erch was now silent. He knew he was in good hands. Callum returned panting, hacksaw in hand, and the

"A Head Case"

blacksmith started sawing just above the head. Soon he was through, and with one spar fractured there was sufficient give to allow the head to be slid painfully out, to the tune of another great howl. A cheer broke out from the spectators, and Jean was profuse in her thanks. Andrew, a man of few words, drew a packet of twenty Players from his pocket, and handed Erch, still rubbing his sores, a cigarette card. It was a picture of a dandelion from the series "Struggles for Existence." Erch clutched his first cigarette card, without knowing he had now made his mark in the street.

Escape

IT WAS summer time and a Saturday. The time for escape
had to come, and this was as good a day as any. Erch was
at his gate, a prisoner, despite the severed spar. In the next
house, not the blacksmith's side, lived Andy, a couple of
months older than Erch. Andy was at his gate. They had
made friends. They had a mutual interest in escape. Hugh
the Post called at Andy's door, and made the fatal mistake of
not shutting the gate. Andy saw his chance. Once free he
pushed at Erch's gate, while Erch pulled. It gave, and Erch
was free also. Hand in hand they headed for the World.
Traffic was no problem, the odd horse and cart and the odd
bicycle, perhaps a steam engine or road roller. Nothing to
worry about. There were dogs of course, and dogs liked little
boys. Jockie, the spaniel mongrel from across the street was
the only witness to the escape, and decided to collaborate.
He joined the adventurers with a woof, and a frantic wagg-
ing of his stump. Jockie resented the slow pace, but at least
he had time to investigate the messages left in such generous measure by his own kind.

The first stop was at Maggie Bain's shop at the corner.
Alas the window was too high and the sweeties could not be
seen. Around the corner, out of sight of home, old crippled
Kyack had a window much lower, and what a fairyland it
contained. Black sugar, toffee sticks and toffee apples,
Cough no More, Sharp's Kreemy, Kings Packets, liquorice
allsorts, Packer's chocolates, snow balls, Devon creams,
and a big, fat black cat. The cat was of no interest to the
twain. It was to Jockie, who, with his forepaws on the
window sill, immediately sighted the enemy. Jockie expressed himself in a tirade of expletive, mixed with dire

threats of evil intent. The contented smirk on puss' face was transformed to wide eyed terror. How could he know how safe he was behind glass? The one thought was of escape. He made a frantic circle round the window, scattering with thrashing paws all the good things sent from Heaven above. An agitated Kyack hobbled to the door, quick enough to clout Jockie over the back with his thick walking stick, reducing the operatic climax to an agonised whimper. Ears back, belly to ground, stump between legs, he beat an undignified retreat. The twain came in for some of Kyack's abuse. Dismayed, they turned their backs to Kyack, and continued on their uncharted way.

Inevitably, they came to the river. The tide was on the flow, the stream a cool, clear reflection of the town. To the east, Cromwell's Fort, the Black Bridge, Lord Roberts' Workshops, the High Kirk, the Free, the Free High, the town Steeple, the Castle. Downstream, but above the Gilbert Street Tannery before which numerous fleeces were anchored in the river bed to be cleansed by the current, the adventurers spied a crowd, a magnet. So, to the crowd at Friars' Shott to watch the salmon fishers at their nets.

This was a social occasion in the neighbourhood at a time when, between Greig Street Bridge and the Black Bull, there were no less than sixty-six residences, against twenty-two today. It was also a neighbourhood which felt only too keenly it was no part of a land fit for heroes. The shadow of deprivation was evident in the dress and demeanour of the crowd. They lived in an area of maximum unemployment, where any free entertainment was welcome. The fishermen were obviously conscious of their role as serious entertainers, and perhaps less obviously conscious of how fortunate they were to be in employment, albeit seasonal. Their work was methodical and purposeful. One, rubber-booted as were all, held the end of the net on the bank. The net was piled high on the stern of the row boat. Two strong pairs of arms pulled the boat out and upstream, and back to the bank in a wide sweep. The net was hauled by all three to the bank.

This is the method of fishing traditionally called in

Scotland "net and cobble." There were four cobble stations in the river. This, the Friars' Shott, stretches back in history to ownership by the Monastery of Dominicans or Black Friars formed in 1233 by Alexander II. We can be reasonably sure the language of the net fishermen was originally Latin, then Gaelic, and at this time, English, or at least "Unverness." Through the centuries the boat, the nets, and the methods suffered little change. We know too that until the present century the River Ness was hotching with salmon.

There was excitement in the crowd, of whom many were boys. A bulge in the net. Two sonsie salmon were extracted, clouted on the head, and deposited in the bottom of the boat.

No single one among that crowd could afford to dine on salmon, now the king of fish, though in earlier days, in its plenteousness, despised even by the most humble. The staple now was Kessock herring, on which a family of six could feed for sixpence.

A voice from the crowd called: –

"Any wee yins, Mister?"

A horny hand dipped into the net, lifted out a small flookie, and threw it high in the air towards the street. A wild scramble of urchins ensued, and at last a wee tough emerged from the scrum chortling with glee, flookie held firmly in both hands. Playfully he held it, still wriggling, up to the face of a little girl at the edge of the crowd. She shouted "Oh gyaadies," and fled.

The twain were entranced by the wonder of this outside world. As they waited expectantly for the next sweep of the nets, an angry looking man in dungarees with shoplach feet bore down on them pushing a bike. It was Andy's Uncle Willie on his way home from work at the "Slip", the Thornbush, where as a labourer for the Rose Street Foundry his job was to help with the construction of the huge floating battleship practice targets for Fleet exercises at Invergordon.

"Home," he said roughly pushing both of them in the back. He walked them home with dark threats of what awaited them there. The only thing they remembered about the journey home was Kyack trying to sort out the chaos in his shop window. Jockie followed, subdued.

Erch and Andy got their bottoms skelped.

School

F ROM the correspondence columns the Old Man read, "'I heard Inverness described as the most beautiful town in the world. Suppose the most beautiful woman we had ever seen, never washed – what would the verdict be?'"

Five was a magic age. At that age it was decreed all children should lose their liberty, get washed and go to school. It was most important to wash the back of the neck and behind the ears. It was there the nosey looked to see whether you came from a clean house.

Traditionally, a new outfit of jersey, shorts, and tie had to be provided, together with a schoolbag. So attired Erch and Andy, with empty schoolbags and fear in their hearts, were led to the Wee School by their Mums. There a concourse of sixes and sevens, excited at the start of a new session and conscious of being old hands, set up a great noise of shouting. They descended upon the newcomers, lined them up against the school wall, and sent up the chant, "Penny bookie, sailor sootie."

Eventually there came the janitor to ring the hand bell, and the doors were opened – one for boys and the other for girls. The chant was changed to "The Bell, the Bell, The Bee, Ell, Ell." Half a dozen teachers descended on the crowd, and in minutes had the children organised, and trooping into school. There was plasticine to play with, and then a half day.

The early months of school were not burdensome. There were games, singing and dancing. Some of the girls were pretty, and it was nice dancing with them. Too often the teacher provided a partner with a face like a horse.

29

Eventually came an introduction to the slate and slate pencil. It was soon found that by holding the pencil at a certain angle, a wonderful screech could be raised, so penetrating it drove the sensitive quite mad.

Come Christmas, there was a Christmas tree and Santa, and a present from the Christmas tree for all. When it was Erch's turn to approach the great man and receive his present, he noticed he was wearing a false face. This was circumstantial evidence to be stored and referred to later. The present was a ball, the size of a man's fist, made of paper, stuffed with sawdust. To it was attached a piece of elastic. Hold the elastic, throw the ball, and it shot back. At the second throw the elastic broke, so he kicked the ball along the road on the way home. The ball burst and the sawdust came out, so there was nothing to show for the first Christmas tree.

The age had also been reached for Sunday school. No Andy for company there. Andy was Free and Erch United Free. So each Sunday, clutching a penny for the plate, Erch followed the inevitable tradition of making an appearance at Sunday school. From the outset he felt he could find better things to do, but his feelings were of no moment. The proprieties had to be observed. One afternoon, en route for Sunday school, he was overcome by a great temptation. There was a small shop kept by an old Catholic lady, Mrs. Kelly, and it was open on Sunday. In the window was black sugar, a reasonable strap of which could be obtained for a ha'penny. The penny was passed over the counter, and in exchange came a strap of black sugar and a ha'penny. How could he have known he was seen entering that den of iniquity on the Sabbath? Jean was waiting. There was only one punishment for such a heinous crime. Down came the trousers.

The only activities permitted on Sunday were attendance at Church and Sunday school. The remainder of the day had to be devoted to the contemplation of eternity or something like that. The safest thing to do was to remain indoors. The neighbours then did not know whether blasphemy or irreverence was being perpetrated, and what they did not know about they could not complain about. It was risky even going for a walk, lest, forgetful, you might contravene the code by picking a bramble, or indulge in any other ungodly practice. And this God was a real busybody of a snooper. He watched for every misdemeanour and wrote it down in a big book in an account kept specially for you. At the Great Day he would pass sentence as soon as he could get his hands on you, and the sentence was bound to be a scorcher. There was no word of credit entries to mitigate the debits and the judgment was in duplicate, because until the Great Day you were also judged by your peers. Their verdict was always "Guilty", and their penalty obloquy.

That afternoon, old Cuthbert, the rabbit trapper who lived over the wall at the back, was heard to be cutting sticks. The neighbourhood was both horrified and scandalised. So flagrantly to flout the Law, ostentatiously and brazenly, deserved but chastisement of the utmost gravity. Early on the Monday morning Cuthbert's collie was heard wailing and Cuthbert was dead.

This was set up as a warning from on High. The Devil got into Erch, was beaten out, and flew into the trapper, who paid the ultimate penalty for his sin.

Match Practice

IT GAVE the Old Man a proud, loyal and parochial Invernessian satisfaction to read: '''A smokeless sunlit Glasgow, and a thriving industrial Inverness are among the developments of the next generation foreshadowed as the outcome of the projected development of the water resources of the Highlands.'''

Erch and Andy had adjoining back yards, each with a small coal shed at the end.

"Whaat footbaal team d'you baak?" said Andy.

Erch had never heard of a football team, and he did not know what was meant by "back."

Not wanting to disclose his ignorance he said, "Ah don't baak any team. Whaat team d'you baak?"

"Caley, of course," said Andy. "Utts th' only team."

"Och well," said Erch, "Ah'll baak Caley too."

So started an interest and an activity that was to go on for years. To kick a ball, there had to be a ball to kick. In Erch's yard, one goal was the coal shed, and the other the wall of the house. Charles liked to participate in all ball games, but he was such a nuisance to serious participants he had to be ordered off. Balls cost money, which was not available, but they could be made. The most primitive was a bundle of newspapers tied with string and this needed constant repair. A refinement was packing newspapers inside an old stocking, and sewing it up so that it would not come unstuck. But it was shapeless. At the most advanced level was a ball of old wool, wound around a shaped fisherman's cork float, and sewn tightly in an old stocking.

The ball was kicked from goal to goal, penalty style, morning before school, dinner time, and after school. The dedication would flatter professionals. Andy's father had actually played for Caley and Andy was therefore a recognised expert. When they wanted to be goalkeepers they threw the ball from end to end, giving opportunity to practise acrobatic saves to their great satisfaction. A mental tally was kept of the score, which in a week could reach three figures. It didn't really matter between mates.

One Saturday morning Andy said, "Goeen t' th' maach?"

"Who's playeen?"

"Caley an' Clach. Ah'll get y' unn wi' ma father."

This sounded great to Erch. Resorting to the water resources of the Highlands and taking a basin of cold water into the back yard, they both scrubbed their faces and knees, remembering backs of necks and behind ears, blacked their boots, and combed out their quiffs. They waited patiently for Andy's Old Man, and sponsored by him they passed the gate guard at Telford Street without the turn of a coin. They took station behind the Distillery goal. Andy knew the names of some of the players, and even the positions in which they played. A howl of welcome went up around the well-filled park when the blue jerseys of Caley took the field. Silence fell on the Distillery when the white jerseys of Clach took the arena, but a counter blast came from the Nursery end. It may be that one game is very much like another. This was a very special game. It was the first. The supporters of both teams were as uninhibited as Highlanders can be, encouraging, cajoling, ridiculing, complaining, applauding. The play went from end to end.

Maclachlan, the tubby Clach right half was not having a very good game and came in for some barracking from his own team's fans midfield. Unable to stand it any longer, he turned to them with outstretched tongue.

Came a voice, raucous from the sideline, "Ach away. Y've got a belly like a brewer's horse." Heady wine.

Sadly for our twain Clach won by three to two.

It became necessary from that day to support Caley. Unsponsored admission cost money. The form was to take station at the boys' gate and bargain for entry. Sometimes the guard was soft and would take a penny against the advertised cost of three dee (threepence or 3d.)

If he were difficult the patter might go ''Four f'r suxpence? Three f'r tuppence? Two f'r a penny?''

Sometimes the guard maintained his stand right up to the kick off. But what enthusiast could keep out a pack of Caley-mad supporters? In the end he always relented, and in went the near penniless, with a penny still in the pocket for chips.

But a way was found around the obstacle of the gate guard. The trainer had to set the nets an hour before the game. He could DO WITH HELP. Erch and Andy became helpers and got in for free, or at least for service. So Andy became independent of his Old Man.

Soon all the players were known by name, and some of them would even give a nod in the street. A nod from a player was a distinction indeed. Players like Frank Bowden, who worked at Lauders Mill in Telford Street, Blyth, Juppy Mitchell, and Sandy Docherty came to recognise the urchins constantly in attendance at home games, and awarded a wink (which was as good as a nod) when meeting them outside the park. That always met with warm response from the hero worshippers.

It was inevitable that street teams should come into being. No league was ever formed, but matches in the Wee Greenie were arranged by challenge. Sometimes in a street game interlopers would demand a game. How they were treated depended on size and strength. If they were big enough they would ruin a game, and they would not try otherwise. After the game the winning team ran pell mell to the *Football Times* office in Hamilton Street to report the score, and gloried to see it in print on Saturday night.

During a match on the Wee Greenie between the Balfairs and Glentoms, four boys from the Shott appeared demanding a game – Tony, Dougie, Willie, and Donnie, all pretty big. It was not cricket to crash a set piece and the argument was coming to a fight, with the smallest of the invaders, Donnie, the most aggressive.

''Aal right,'' said Donnie, ''You tek thaat gadgie Tony, you tek this gadgie Dougie, you tek this gadgie Willie, an aal

34

tek this gadgie an nokk hus paan off.''

Allocations clearly favoured the invaders, each of whom was allotted a lighter opponent. There was silence for a moment.

Then Andy advanced to Donnie on guard, ''Aal rite. You tek thus gadgie.''

Andy gave him fugee – a few innocuous jabs on the chest to get his dander up. Donnie never expected such a spirited response from one so much smaller than he, and now looking so menacing in anger. He realised he had underrated his victim and refused to put up his guard. Thus ended the invasion of which Andy was the hero.

But a short argument ensued.

Donnie said, ''Ah'll get ma uncle t'you. He's unn th' poleece.''

''Och, Ah've got an uncle a sojer. He's bigger than your uncle.''

''Bet he's not,'' said Donnie.

''Bet he is,'' said Andy.

''Bet he's not,'' said Donnie, and then farted. ''That's proof.'' For some strange reason the last assertion with its reinforcement became incontrovertible, so Donnie did not lose face completely.

The ambition of every boy was to play for the school. To be handed out a jersey with red and yellow stripes was the thrill of a lifetime. Andy and Erch got theirs the same day and Jean insisted on washing Erch's right away for fear of nits. They wore their jerseys at practice in the back yard, as well as at games.

The school team was well supported by both pupils and teachers, and the Caley Park was made available for home matches. Friday afternoon was the traditional day and time.

In the inter-school league were Central, Merkinch, Farraline Park, Bishop's Boys, Leachkin, High and Academy. Because the Academy Primary was so small, they were allowed to select from the first year secondary, but it never did them much good, and often as not they could not field a full team. The Bishop's Boys was a very small school, but they always competed, though seldom with success.

The Leachkin was poor at football but came into their own at shinty, spurred on by their headmaster, then John MacQueen, a great enthusiast and respected by all. The league was dominated by Farraline Park, Merkinch and Central, and of these probably the first two were most successful. Despite rivalries, the school league gave rise to lasting friendships which could not be built otherwise.

The school provided a real ball and the Wee Greenie was the venue for practices. When the school ball was not available, and it was only with a master in attendance, perhaps a tennis ball or a sorbo could be found. The sorbo was unburstable, the size of a tennis ball, and usefully resistant to tackety boots. For the most part everybody who turned up played, and each chose his own side in the free for all.

Football was also played in the street, to the alarm of householders whose windows were at risk. A sharp eye had to kept for the Bobby on the beat, who was usually Kenny the Masher.

His admonition was "Scachter boys. Scachter."

In that situation it was easy to avoid his long reach. It was different for the miserable sinner caught up a lamp post. There was no bargaining. The penalty was a dalacher round the lug, rather as a token than a punishment.

Callum and Dougal were playing at "shooting in" with a sorbo. A strong shot by Callum went straight and true for Shivas' window, and knocked it in with a clatter. There was no-one in sight so Callum and Dougal were down the street and round the corner before the glass stopped falling. They walked in leisurely fashion round the block and were back in ten minutes to commiserate with poor Shivas, who was contemplating in sorrow and anger the wreck of his window. While publicly denying all knowledge of the culprit, they privately mourned the loss of the sorbo.

Shinty sticks were expensive, but Torvean hill would always provide the enterprising with a stick with a crook at the end. A winter Saturday morning was the time for shinty and play often took place in frost and snow. To keep

36

the blood flowing, the fingers which clutched the stick required constant rubbing, and the arms had often to be slapped around the body. Though shinty looks a wild game it gives rise to few serious accidents, but, with a small hard ball flighted far, requires space, and pitches were found at the Victoria Park (the Pub) on the triangle between Glenurquhart Road and Bruce Gardens. The shinty team had practically no following for it was Saturday, and it was cold.

Park Road, Smith Avenue, Lindsay Avenue, Maxwell Drive and Bruce Avenue did not then exist. There were no houses on the west side of Glenurquhart Road from Park Road south to the Cemetery Lodge.

Of an evening, as dark was falling, the tired players were making their way home by Bruce Gardens. A field of turnips by the roadside on Tomnahurich Farm was too much of a temptation. They helped themselves, bit off the skins, and were soon enjoying the earthy juicy sweetness. Before long an angry man on a bike, with a big black moustache and carrying a stick, followed by a collie dog, descended on them. He gave of himself so expressively, supported as he was by a dog and a stick, that the boys were immediately reduced to remorse. He took all their names, and warned that a repetition would mean the ''Poleece.'' They could not know they were in the presence of one of the greatest fiddlers and fiddle makers the Highlands have ever known, and the inventor of the spliced vibration fishing rod used throughout the length and breadth of Scotland. It was Alex Grant, founder of the Strathspey and Reel Society, and tenant of Tomnahurich.

For a match with Bell's School (Farraline Park) at the ramparts at the Citadel, a faded symbol of Cromwell's strength, only five of the team turned up. Bell's lent one or two players and won 21 – 0. Horror of horrors, the headmaster witnessed the last fifteen minutes of the game. On the Monday following the missing team members were paraded before a very irate head – a stickler for discipline. They were banned from a place in the team for the rest of the season since they had spent their Saturday morning having,

37

"KALAKADOOGIE"

they thought, better fun, sliding on the frozen pavements. No cup that year. A severe penalty for a kalakadoogie – a slide in near sitting position on the ice and a turn through three hundred and sixty degrees.

Finance

"ANDY, ANDY, Andy, Andy."
Erch was calling at Andy's back door in the conventional manner of raising a mate. Older boys would have whistled their own particular signal, round mouthed or fingers between teeth. For them that sophistication lay in the future.

Andy appeared eating a piece of bread and crowdie, the fag end of his tea.

"Whaat's up?" asked Andy.

"Fancy a gemme of punky?"

"Don't mind."

Andy retreated indoors, returning with his bag of marbles. The punky hole had already been shaped in Erch's yard, and play commenced.

"Goeen t' th' match t'morrow?" asked Andy.

"Who's playeen?"

"Caley an' Citadel, Caley Park. Big gemme. Bound t' be a crowd."

"Wouldn't mind, b't ah w's planning the baths unn th' morneen."

"Y'll have t' pay t' gett unn t' th' baths."

"Aye, an' ah canna pay both. Got you. That's three. Y' owe me one durb."

Dutifully Andy handed over one durb, fairly rooched. It was the most miserable one in his collection. Play recommenced.

"How much w'll y' hev?" asked Andy.

"Thruppence."

40

"Ah'll only hev tuppence."

"Hev y' anytheen unn y'r pose box?"

"Aye," said Erch, "Hev aabout a tanner unn pennies and ha'pennies."

"Y' cood slide some of utt out wi' a knife."

"Wush ah cood. Old Man put flaps inside the slutt. When ah've got a penny balanced on the knife and try t' gett utt out, th' flaps push utt off. Ah c'n only gett utt open at Christmas. Hev t' melt th' soldurr on th' gaas."

Andy thought again.

"Might gett two f'r tuppence at th' match if Jock Mackenzie's on th' gett. But we'll no gett past Boomer at th' baths f'r less th'n thruppence."

"No. Try any trucks on humm an' we'll no gett unn at aal. But Jock Mackenzie's always on th' boys' gett," said Erch. "He might keep us t'll th' gemme starts, but he's a good sort. He always guves unn, unn th' end."

"Aye. Wonder if anyone wants messuges."

"Nobody wants messuges on a Friday nite."

"No, but furst thing unn th' morneen."

Erch reflected that the time for the baths was 10 a.m. Time before then for messages.

"We'll try Mrs. Greig. She always wants messuges on a Sa'urday morneen."

"We're safe enuff ther," conceded Erch, "But that's only a penny."

"What about jam jars or lemunade bo'les?"

"Ma mother always keeps th' jam jars f'r th' home made, an' we never buy lemunade."

Andy was wracking his brains to find a way of raising the wind.

"What about swappmg some theen?"

"What's th' use o' that. Wouldn't gett us any munny."

"We'd hev t' find someone who c'd pay. I know – Ian. He getts a tanner a week, an' he was planning buying glassacks unn Walkers t'morrow."

"Great idea. He'd hev t' pay Walkers a tanner f'r three. We cood give humm four f'r tuppence."

They both tipped the durbs from their bags on to the

ground, and spread them to pick out the glassacks. Between them they had eight, but two were chipped. They examined the chippies critically, and agreed they could not be palmed off on Ian.

''C'm on Andy. Let's give them a wash, an' go t' see Ian now.''

Away they went, a major financial problem having been solved. They would be in the baths in the morning, and at the match in the afternoon.

The River

W HEN YOU were ever so young, the streets, the churches, the Castle, the houses and shops, and the important people were as they always were, and always would be, or so it seemed. If you were born on the outside looking in, were you ever likely to be on the inside?

Summers were long. Sometimes there was sunshine for days on end, and sometimes there was rain, especially when it came on St. Swithin's day, then there was six solid weeks of it.

Andy was rattling away at his peter-dick trying to get a tune like the kettle drummers in the British Legion Band, and not making a very good job of it. He had already tried on the crackers, but he felt his instrument was the peter. Pity it did not make more noise. Erch was trying to whistle "Ramona," all the rage with the bowshers, and not making a very good job of it. He had already tried it on the wee saucer shaped whistle about the size of a ha'penny which sometimes came in a Lucky packet. He gave up that some time ago, after Hector MacPhee. Hector had swallowed a whistle like that, and it took four days to pass right through him. Hector showed it as a trophy, like a past (or passed) master, but did not use it again. Tissue paper on a comb was better.

"I know where to get the biggest sliders for a penny," said Andy. A slider was an ice cream between two wafers.

"Where?"

"Bickers', of course," said Andy.

They were both armed with a penny, and made for King Street. As they passed Smith the Joiner's back door the huge English sheep dog sprang out at them, barking. He was on

43

THE MUSIC MAKERS

a chain and could not reach his quarry but certainly did give the boys a fright. Ambling down Bickers' Lanie, they reached Huntly Street. The pennies were proferred to Mrs Bickers, who doled out handsome sliders to each. They were good.

There were fairly frequent parades to Mrs Bickers' shoppie for sliders in summer, and home made toffee in winter. The toffee came in a large tray and it was fascinating to see Mrs Bickers break it up with a hammer. There was no question of weighing. She judged by eye a fair quantity for a penny, and put it in a poke which she deftly screwed up from a flat piece of paper.

To the boys Mrs Bickers was an old lady, though in fact she was probably only in her mid-fifties. She was slow on her feet, possibly suffering from the malady which seemed to afflict so many elderly people – rheumatism. She had a stoop, and a pleasant round face topped by a bunch of unruly grey hair, not fully under control of her hair pins. Behind her wire-rimmed spectacles were a pair of twinkling eyes.

Mrs Bickers was very fond of pigeons, and she fed them in the street fronting the shop, calling "Peesie, peesie, peesie." Traffic was nearly non existent. The odd cyclist, hawker with hurley, or cart driver would make a detour to avoid Mrs Bickers' pigeon feeding time. On one occasion when the twain were on their usual business, Mrs Bickers had in her hands a pigeon with a damaged leg. She could not hold the bird and bind the leg at the same time so aid was required. Erch willingly held the bird while she tied a rag around the leg and the reward was a free slider. Mrs Bickers' business acumen was not the stuff from which fortunes are made.

Opposite Bickers' shoppie was a stone jetty in the river. This marked the highest point to which the salmon fishers operated their boats, just below the Suspension Bridge, although the river was tidal as far as the Infirmary Bridge.

"Let's wade," said Andy.

They took off their sandshoes and socks, hung them round their necks, and began to wade to the middle of the stream. The tide was out and the water not deep. It was deep enough, however, to require that the short trouser legs be rolled up, and even then they were at risk.

"You're toucheen!" shouted Erch, and Andy pulled his trouser legs up as high as he could.

When you are holding up your trouser legs and wading on slippery stones, you have no arms for balance. Andy stumbled and fell. Erch, close by, tried to hold him and they both went prostrate in the water. The thrill went out of wading. They found after total immersion that they were very cold. The first complete immersion in the river. One-third the way to qualification as a true Clacher.

Miserably they headed back for the jetty, and donned their sandshoes to make for home. They were not unobserved. Simey the Sneak, about their own age, got great pleasure from their predicament, gleefully leering.

"You'll get belted when you get home."

The thought had some truth, which made it all the more objectionable. But Jock the Donal, slightly older than the pair, was friendlier disposed.

"C'm on t' Androo the Smuth's an' get dried," said Jock.

When they reached Andrew's he had the hind leg of a whacking great Clydesdale between his legs, and was about to clamp on a hot shoe. When he did so a cloud of white smoke issued from the hoof. Andy remembered it was a grand smell.

"Gett ovur ther tull ah'm redy," said the smith.

The three stood in a corner of the smiddy in near darkness, among heaps of rusty iron and nails. Eventually the great Clydesdale was led out, quite passive, to be attached to the Wordie's lorry standing in the street outside. Wordie had the contract for deliveries from the railway.

"Stan' ther," said Andrew. "You c'n blow," he said addressing Jock.

This was what Jock wanted. He heaved on the bellows, and the forge came up bright. The two waders pirouetted slowly in front of the heat. Then Andrew re-appeared from the yard behind, and dismissed them.

"Away wi' yuh. An' dinna faal unn th' ruvvur agen."

They had a bonus, for they saw the famous blackbird's nest within six feet of the anvil; mother blackbird successfully reared three young amidst all the clamour of the blacksmith's shop.

They were soon back in the river again, with the Balfair Street gang, building a street castle. The Shott castle was opposite the High Kirk, and it was a big one that had to be outstripped. There were many hands – well at least twelve. The older boys were the master masons, and knew that a wide circular base was required for a start. It took several days to finish the job, but there was a respectable castle when completed, as big as the Shott one, and the Shott boys were quick to notice this. They descended like wolves on the fold, and Balfair were not strong enough for them. There was a brief struggle in mid-stream and soon the Balfair castle was levelled to the bottom of the river.

Despondency.

What to do but plot revenge? The following day about 1 p.m. twelve from Balfair thought the coast was clear. They crossed the Greig Street bridge and descended on the rival castle. But there was a watcher. A shrill call was heard – "SHOTTIES!" The Shotties appeared as from nowhere and splashed into the river to defend their masterpiece. Only one stone had been displaced when the meeting took place and the Shotties were not so good natured in defence as in attack. All the Balfairs were ducked, and retreated in disarray. A second ducking then, and two-thirds the way to becoming a Clacher.

There was no point in going in such strength to the smiddy, but Jock the Donal had another idea. Noble the carpenter's yard. At Noble's yard Jeem the apprentice was stoking a great fire of shavings and wood chips. Jeem had just got in to longeens – long trousers. It was only a boiler suit over his shorts, but they were longeens, man's attire. Furthermore, he had a cloth cap, another sign of years advancing to manhood. His manly reserve had to be broken, but blood was thicker than water and Jock the Donal was his cousin. Jeem let the vanquished Balfairs stand in front of his fire until they felt they were dry enough.

The next momentous moment for Erch was towards the end of the summer holidays. Ian had come to live at the top of the street. His father was a commercial traveller, and did not dirty his hands. The family had the only wireless set in the street, with a great big horn and an aerial between the two chimneys and they also had two buckets, with lids.

Ian was a bit more refined than the usual Balfairs. He had a scoobie – a five foot length of bamboo cane, with a little net on the end.

"How about going to the river to catch parrs?" said Ian.

That was a good idea and away they went.

There had been days of rain and the streets were wet. The great elms between the riverside road and the cathedral road were beginning to cast a leaf. Ian knew about the stone horse above one of the cathedral windows, and pointed it out to Erch, feeling rather superior. "That horse was killed at the building of the Cathedral," said Ian. Erch gawked in open-eyed wonder, and in his mind's eye saw the poor horse lying on its side with piles of fallen masonry on top of him. It was nice of them to put the wee horse up there.

At that time, as now, the two parallel roads were on different levels, the disparity increasing as they moved upstream. They were separated by a flat topped stone dyke, the height of which at the cathedral end was nil, gradually increasing to about three feet at its southern extremity, opposite Bishop's Road. The elms grew alongside the dyke, and it was inevitable that the path of the young was always by way of the top of the dyke.

The route led by the Whirlie Gatie – a pedestrian access marked by a post standing three feet six inches high, topped by a rotating cross of solid batons. It was important to push them clockwise when passing through, otherwise the Devil might be roused, and he was never far away.

Ian had been before to the Whirlie Gatie, which guarded the Bught entrance to the Islands, just beside the White Stonies. The roadway did not extent southwards beyond Ballifeary House. Ian said the Whirlie Gatie was lucky, so, for safety, they both made a wish and passed through. They walked upstream, past the General's Well, by the mill lade,

48

to the black shed where the electricity was made. Right below was a deep hole where fish could always be seen but never caught — they were too distant for a net and too timid for a hook. The shed which first fed electricity to the Burgh of Inverness, courtesy of Edmundson's Electricity Corporation Limited, stood in the shadow of the derelict old mill. But the river was in spate, no time for catching what Ian called parrs, and Erch called beelans. There were one or two quiet pools holding sticklebacks and these were fetched into Ian's jar.

The boys wandered homewards, hugging the river bank. About opposite the Infirmary the bank, though steep at the roadside, levelled out towards the water, and they stopped there for a rest. They sat on stones, and Ian showed Erch how to make mirrors with grass and spittles. They had a competition to see who could make the biggest mirror. Ian won easily. They played sojers, in the style of conkers, with ribwort. They got some small flat stones from the roadside and Ian showed Erch how to make skeetchers — bouncing the flatties on the surface of the deep and fast flowing river. Ian got up as far as eight stots, but Erch could get no more than six. When they became tired, they decided to have a last throw to decide once and for all who was the better.

Erch placed himself on the edge of the bank for his last and greatest endeavour. He put so much into that last throw that his body followed his missile and in he went, splash, into the deep raging stream. This was different from the last two immersions. This was life or death. He could not reach the bottom, and even if he could, the spate would not allow him a foothold. He was carried helpless down past the Infirmary Bridge, and took in several involuntary gulps of river. Ian ran after him, scoobie in one hand, and sticklebacks in the other. The stickles were soon lost in the frantic chase.

Erch screamed "Help," and took in another mouthful.

The wits were scared out of him. Then he saw Ian on the bank, so near and yet so far.

In desperation he called out to him, "Stick out y'r scoobie!"

Ian, still on the trot, stuck out his bamboo, and Erch was

LANDING
A BIG CATCH

just able to grasp it. The little net fell off, but what mattered a net in such a crisis. Ian pulled him in, and he clutched at the long grass, hoisting himself with no dignity on to dry land, overlooked by the little stone horse, whom he might have joined with the angels.

There he lay for a few minutes, panting, no thought in his head but to get himself home, and that as quick as his shaky legs would carry him. No smiddy entered his head. Just to get home, tears running down his face, fear clutching his belly.

There had been many warnings – "Keep away from the river." If the day dawns when boys can be kept away from rivers, then there will no longer be any boys.

When the bedraggled apparition arrived home, Jean saw this was not the result of some ordinary ploy. She was sympathetic, kindly, frightened perhaps, but not angry. She stripped him and put him in the enamel bath in front of the cinders, sponging the comforting warm water over his body. Then she towelled him and put him to bed.

Erch did not rejoice he was now three times immersed, and a full blown Clacher.

He turned his face to the wall, clenched his fists, and muttered aloud, "Ah must lern t' swum."

And then he slept.

Swimming

THE BOYS in the Big School got into the baths free on Tuesday afternoons, and during the summer holidays, Monday, Tuesday, and Wednesday mornings.

The Balfair short cut to the baths was through the Wee Greenie, and over the dyke to the tennis courts in Montague Row which adjoined the baths. "Courts" is a flattering word to use. It really was a pretty rough bit of grass, sophistication in that rather elegant sport not having reached Inverness at that time.

The baths were privately owned by the laundry company, and were twenty-five yards long by twelve-and-a-half wide. They were heavily subsidised by the town council. They were tiled round the sides and on the bottom, and a cast iron rail ran round the side just above the water level. Many of the tiles were cracked, and more were broken. The shallow end was two-and-a-half feet deep, and the deep end seven feet. There were a spring board and diving boards and along one side was a range of cubicles for dressing, each of which might be in use by up to four boys at a time. Mixed bathing had not arrived, nor had Sunday swimming. Boys could wear trunks, but men were required to wear a full costume.

A line of eight inch cast iron rings suspended from ropes fixed to the roof ties ran the length of the bath. It was possible to swing, Tarzan-like, from the deep end to the shallow. Most who tried found that in the middle, there was a low ring, difficult to grasp, and their enterprise ended in a ducking. There were dare-devils who did the rings with their clothes on. Few escaped disaster. Every Saturday afternoon the baths were drained, brushed down, and refilled. The muck on the bottom of the pool by Saturday,

52

the sweat from hundreds of bodies, was revolting. The baths were only opened during the summer months and the water was always cold.

The Old Man was sympathetic towards swimming. He himself had learned in the dirty pool at the Carse, in the triangle between canal and railway. His were the days before pollution, when the pool was both clean and safe. He readily responded when a pair of swimming trunks were required at ninepence, and was equally willing to part with three dee (if not overdone) for admission when funds did not otherwise permit. Erch and Andy being still in the Wee Schoolie, had no free passes. There was no question of barter here as at football. Guard was kept by the Boomer, a middle aged gentleman, florid of face, sad white moustache, and thin grey hair which stood up like a cone in the middle of his crust. He watched through a little window which looked out on to the vestibule entrance, he kept the laundry books, and no doubt managed as well. He probably had very good reason for being testy.

"Youse boys mek up y'r minds. Ef y' waant t' gett unn, pey y'r thruppence an' gett unn. Ef y' hevn't gott thruppence, get t' hell oota heer."

For his first season Erch attended regularly, and did no more than cling to the rail at the shallow end, shivering and terrified to let go. The braver hearts frolicked around, and indulged in all kinds of horse play. Every return from the baths was made in despondency. Yet at home, dry land exercises were performed daily, and Erch, in his imagination, swam length after length, to the envy of his mates.

At the beginning of his second season the Old Man presented Erch with a pair of water wings. The idea was that they gradually lost buoyancy, and eventually left the swimmer on his own. With the wings for support, Erch was early off his feet, and was soon swimming a good breast stroke with, and not long after, without, wings.

The passion for swimming transcended that for all other activities. To Erch, the greatest of social occasions was an evening gala in the baths, at which he watched enraptured his heroes of speed, style, and polo. Sometimes experts from afar demonstrated. Mr and Mrs Allan from Aberdeen were favourites. Mrs Allan wore a black costume stretching from ankles to neck, and dived gracefully. Mr Allan, little handicapped by reason of having only one leg, swam stylish and relaxed, demonstrating the various strokes then in vogue – breast, back, side, overarm side, and trudgeon. The crawl was practically unknown.

Then came a time of great sadness. The baths closed for ever. There were many who felt bereaved. Dirty and cold they might have been, but they met the vital need of many enthusiasts whose hunger could not be fully requited in the great outdoors under a grey and fluid sky.

Erch and his mates looked for outdoor swimming. Bunchrew was three miles to walk, but it was worth it for a swim. The drawback was that the tide had to be in. Then they found Burnfoot in the canal – a little sandy bay near to where the paddle boats Gondolier and Glengarry laid up for the winter. It was cold and it was dangerous but by now Andy and Erch were both swimming reasonably well, confident on a breast stroke, and knew no fear of the water. Once they were among a group of young swimmers at Burnfoot when Cock-eyed Beelan came on the scene, towel rolled up under his wing, strutting with his usual swagger. He had just entered his teens. He quickly stripped and announced he was going to swim across the canal. Some of his age group tried to dissuade him, but he was determined. He struck out strongly on his breast, and as he got nearer the middle his strokes became faster and faster, and faster and shorter, more erratic and weaker, until he was ready to admit defeat. His agonised cries for help brought out two boatbuilders from the canal workshop alongside. Both had been in the old water-polo team. They stripped to their drawers and swam to the rescue with powerful trudgeon strokes, but by the time they reached the area of Beelan's disaster, his cries were douched, and he was nowhere to be seen. Beelan's bravado was his undoing. He never breathed again.

Burnfoot and the canal were abandoned for swimming for

the time being. The sight of Beelan going to the bottom sent a cold chill down the spines of the youngsters. The place of tragedy was no more for them.

Beelan's body was recovered at night when it rose to the surface.

The Courier recorded the incident with great sympathy, but its readers could not have the same horrified interest which possessed Erch and Andy.

Tomnahurich, The Hill Of The Fairies

ERCH AND ANDY had completed their ninth summer in 1924, all in Balfair Street.

Opposite them lived old Shivas, a surface-man in the railway, who had got a touch of gas in the war. Poor old Shivas was often sick.

The boys met at their doors after breakfast.

"Look," said Andy, pointing to Shivas' windows.

The yellow blinds were drawn. Fascinated, they stared at the windows, and the big front door, which was tight shut.

"He must be dedd," said Erch in hushed tone.

The day of the funeral all the blinds in the street were drawn, but in adjoining houses there were two small boys watching between the chinks in the blinds. A thought was formulating in Erch's head. His curiosity was not going to stop there.

Shivas was well liked and well known. He was in the British Legion and a piper turned out in Dress Stewart Tartan. The Freemasons were all dressed up in aprons and sashes, with things hanging round their necks. The church people, the railwaymen and all the neighbours attended. There could be no question of all these people getting into Shivas' little parlour. There were fully a hundred and one dog, Jockie, the spaniel mongrel, usually a great favourite in the street but today ignored. He smelt around for the accustomed clap. Receiving none, he too was sad. The undertaker, Dow the Dedd, had his horses beautifully groomed for the hearse and three cabs. He moved unobtrusively among the mourners, and laid the flowers in the little garden patch fronting the house. On the fringe of the crowd stood Big Hector the Bobby, all six-feet-two of him, possessed of the kindest of good natures, and the biggest feet in town.

The Reverend Allison arrived wearing his black soup plate hat, his black moustache trimmed and his red nose shining. He went into the house, and soon reappeared at the gate. Hat in hand, he put on his gold rimmed pince-nez, and peered through the oval glasses to find the place in his little black book. Encouraged by Dow, the party gathered round. There was a reading and a prayer, and "The Lord's my Shepherd." The vocal endeavours did not match the noble words. The keys employed were varied, and the erratic tempo reflected the several kirk backgrounds of the mourners.

After the benediction, the Reverend tucked his book into a poacher's pocket, leaving Dow to arrange the piper and the masons at the front of the hearse. Old Shivas was brought out of his parlour in his wooden box, the brass handles gleaming in the sunlight. The women of the family came out of the door to bid their last farewell, for never did the womenfolk follow the cortège. The flowers were placed in the hearse and one of the cabs, and two grown sons took the next cab, leaving the third for the minister. The bowler hats formed up behind, one or two tiles among them.

Unhurried, Dow saw that all was in order before he nodded to Gavin the Hearse, and the piper to make a move. The piper started off with "Over the Sea to Skye" in slow time, because Shivas' mother came from Glendale. Malkie the Milkman on his rounds, stopped his horse, went to its head, and removed his cap while the procession passed by.

Then the blinds were up and Andy and Erch were free again.

They were drawn as by a magnet to follow at a very respectful distance, hoping no-one would notice. The pace was ever so slow, and the cemetery entrance was by the Glenurquhart Road gate. Instinctively they felt it unbecoming to follow into the cemetery. They turned back, and ran for the nearest gate of the public park, and placed themselves at the railings which separated it from the cemetery. At somewhat long range they watched the remainder of the ceremony, and the dispersal of the mourners. They turned for home, silent and feeling rather empty.

Spirits could not remain low for long at that age.

"Bet y' wouldn't go into th' cemetery at nite," said Erch. There was no immediate reply.

"Bet you wouldn't," said Andy. Another pause.

"Bet I would," said Erch, "I will go tonite."

Andy felt a bit shocked, but he did not like to be bettered. "Aal rite, we'll both go," he said.

They were both somewhat dumbfounded by the enormity of their plan, but pride was pride, and they were both too stubborn to admit home was a better place on a dark night.

After tea, and it was herring for both that evening, they met in Erch's back yard. Andy brought out his sorbo and they started to play, each trying to show the other he had not a care in the world. Much sooner than they expected, the light failed and they could not see the ball.

"C'm on then," said Andy, and they set off at a trot for the Glenurquhart Road gate. The plan was to walk right through to the Bruce Gardens gate. Tomnahurich Cemetery is located on and around a heavily wooded hill, lying like an upturned boat, extending a little over four hundred and fifty yards north to south and a little less east to west. The name is rooted in folklore. There lie Fienn, the three giants of Scotland awaiting a bugle call to rise and free the land. As the ice moved northwards from the Great Glen, it left this great deposit of sand and rubble. It is admirably suited to the function it serves, but in the darkness of the night it is indeed an eerie place. Some called it the Hill of the Fairies, but some thought more appropriate would be the Hill of the Leprechauns. There were guard houses at both ends of the route, with a cemetery mannie occupying each. MacColl at the Bruce Gardens end was the one to fear. He was said to be wild.

The night was dark, and without Lochiel's lantern, the moon, the widespread gas lamps did little to dispel the gloom. The tall iron gates filling the gap in the iron perimeter fence with its murderous spikes, were locked to keep out those who had no right to be in, and to keep in those who had no right to be out. One hour after sunset was the rule. The road was deserted. They climbed the eight feet gate, carefully easing themselves over the spikes. Andy's jersey caught on a spike and he had a moment of fright before he freed it. They gently lowered themselves down to the forbidden ground. They crouched momentarily, checking that so far they were undetected. There was a gaslight burning behind the blinds in the windows of the cemetery mannie's house, but not a sound. The outside roadway was deserted, and they turned their faces north to the Bruce Gardens end, not half a mile distant.

Round the base of the hill they walked gingerly, not to make a noise, though they were not clear in their own minds whom they did not wish to disturb. Would the fiddlers be awake? Would the tinkers march tonight? Would the Stewart Kings of Scotland arise? Would the Provost be there in his red robes and cocked hat? These were old wives' tales and daft.

The going was open at first, and as their eyes became accustomed to the dark, they did not feel too uneasy. They soon found, however, that Tomnahurich Hill was closing in on them, and the big black trees overshadowed their path. The gravestones stood silently to right and to left, and in front, mute guardians over their charges. Most stones were granite, and sombre in colour. Rounding a bend in the pathway they came upon a tall white stone. There were two sharp involuntary intakes of breath, but it was only a stone, and on they went. There was a rustle among the leaves, and they unwittingly drew closer to each other. A bird. The heavy branches of the ancient elms creaked as they submitted to the rising breeze. It wasn't so much fun as they thought it was going to be.

A rabbit scurried across their path, its white patches showing up all too clearly. Their hearts were now in their mouths, and to cap it all another rabbit came straight for them, and they stopped in their tracks. At a range of three feet they appeared to be observed, and the animal brushed their legs and made a sharp right turn towards the hill,

59

TOMNAHURICH.
"BOGLES AND GHAISTIES"

scattering leaves to right and to left, sending a spine-chilling shiver down their backs.

By now they were demoralised, but they had passed the point of no return, well more than half way, and still facing their goal. They stuttered on, the hill and its black threatening trees bending down on them with every step, to blot out what little light remained in an overcast sky. There was a frantic flapping of powerful wings accompanied by the unmistakable "Hoo! Hoo!" Then the brute changed its call as owls do to the terrifying and piercing "EWEE! EWEE!" They paused for a moment frozen to the spot.

"Gees!" said Erch, his knees like jelly. Then without a spoken word, they ran pell mell, like all the devils in hell were after them, burst through MacColl's wee private gate, through his garden without respect to cultivations, and out his street gate to the public road and its dim gaslights.

Vaguely they heard behind them in the darkness the shouts of the angry MacColl, thirsting for blood, and the barking of his big mongrel dog. One hundred yards, two, three they ran, heads down, right into the blue arms of Big Hector. The arms of the Law in the shape of Hector, far from being the cause of further terror, were a blissful refuge. The boys, gulping great bellyfuls of leprechaun free air, released themselves to bend double over the farm fence alongside. Stomachs in rebellion, they catapulted two undigested loads of salt herring into the turnips.

Next day was to be a day for bragging, but no pride could be taken in their escapade. By mutual consent, mum was the word. No-one was to know of their visit to the fairies by night. No-one did – until now.

Over The Ferry

TO PICNIC over the ferry was at all times a great adventure. There being no other transport, a horse cab was hired to traverse the mile-long road from town centre to pier. The elders piled inside with baskets and bags of goodies, and a kettle for the tea. The boys proudly perched on the "dickie" beside the driver, and clip clopped by Grant Street and the Clach Football Ground, under the railway bridge, past the Thornbush harbour, the coastguard signal station, and the old brewery, to the south pier, where the *Lowestoft Belle* puffed impatiently.

The skipper on the bridge wore a cutter cap, naval style, the deck hands puffed their bogie roll as they tended the moorings, and the engineer-cum-stoker, head only visible above the engineroom hatch, clutched an oily rag with which he rubbed coal dust off or into his burnished brow. The smell was exquisite – a mixture of sea ware, coal smoke, steam, oil, and a whiff of bogie roll.

All aboard, the Skipper's orders rang out – "Let go forrad, let go aft," a warning hoot on the whistle, the bell of the engineroom telegraph and its answer from below, the pistons clanked, and away went the *Belle* to Valhalla. She could carry a few sheep and cattle. Cars were no problem because there were none.

Above were the screaming gulls, which fed on the succulent Kessock herring, and the calls of the curlew and the oyster catcher were sometimes heard in the gaps between the gulls' din – those rude gulls which shot so straight at summer hats.

There could be a couple of swans around the north side, but what was hoped for was porpoises, those good natured tumblers which so often escorted the *Belle* on her way, racing ahead, circling, unafraid to show themselves, and fully entering into the spirit of the picnic. Sharks have been known too, but unlike the tumblers they kept well away from the boat. A seal might have a sly peep. The scene was probably little changed since the first steamboat plied the ferry in 1862. Clothes would have differed, but the smells, the birds, and the creatures of the sea were constant.

In the early twenties, Mr Roderick Maclennan started running charabanc-type buses to the ferry from the town centre, but through ill health abandoned the business in 1927, when one of his drivers Mr William Greig took over. By 1933, Mr Greig, then a very successful operator, was refused permission to use double-deckers on the service. Such an innovation would constitute a danger in the narrow streets of Inverness, and they were so tall they would surely topple. It was only a matter of time before the security of the cabbies would be in jeopardy.

The retirement of the ferry boat was to be a slower process. A ferry bridge was proposed to relieve unemployment in 1922. There were then 504 out of work in the town which had a population of 20,937.

Meantime the *Lowestoft Belle* was suffering from rheumatism, arthritis, hip joint disease, *ennui*, and every other symptom of antiquity. More and more frequently arose occasions when she was unable to perform her ferry functions, until in March 1936 she was withdrawn, and a very inferior service was provided by open motor boat.

The right to operate the ferry was vested in the proprietor of the estates of Kessock in Inverness, and Craigton in the Black Isle, Provost Sir Donald Macdonald, owner of an importing business in Inverness. He was a man much respected in the locality, for thirty years a member of council, and the Provost who welcomed Lloyd George's cabinet which met in the Town Hall, Inverness, in 1921 to discuss the "Irish Question." Sir Donald died in March 1934 and the ferry rights passed to Mr William Macdonald. Poor man. He was to wish he had never heard of the ferry.

In anticipation of the demise of the *Lowestoft Belle*, Mr

63

William Macdonald purchased a replacement boat, which, en route from the Clyde, sank off the Argyll coast in February 1936. It was a total wreck, and uninsured.

Mr Macdonald purchased a second boat chain ferry type, which set out by the west coast from Cornwall, only to be wrecked in April 1936 off St. Agnes Head, to sink in nineteen fathoms.

He then arranged for the *S.S. Ailsa* to serve temporarily. *Ailsa* was as substantial as the old *Belle*, and more powerful. She had been running the ferry service between Cromarty and Invergordon, to a dwindling demand. She also ran popular cruises from Inverness to Cromarty, Nigg, and Invergordon, especially when the Home Fleet was based at Invergordon for autumn exercises. She could not take cars, a demand which was growing at Kessock. A small private car could be bought for £125, and commercial interests were deserting the old horse in favour of vans and motor lorries. The *Ailsa* served for little over a month, and in October 1936 Mr Macdonald announced he would have a new and adequate vessel on the service within two weeks.

The new vessel reached Banavie at the western end of the Caledonian Canal, and was found to be too broad in the beam to negotiate the locks. Unsuccessfully, Mr Macdonald sought government assistance, and withdrew the service.

But by March 1937 he was in the market again, and a fourth boat commenced its journey from the Clyde by the northern route, this time under tow. It safely negotiated the Pentland Firth but its diabolic fortune was to sink off Tarbat Ness, almost within sight of its destination.

The members of the community most affected by the poor ferry service were the residents of the Black Isle. Many of these commuted to Inverness to work, and they turned towards the town for shopping, various necessary services, and entertainment. They had to admit Mr Macdonald stretched himself to meet his obligation as owner of the ferry rights, but irrespective of that, they were without that vital link required to join north and south piers. They organised large protest meetings which got wide press coverage.

In February 1938 a public demonstration was held, when

Mr Macdonald claimed to have acquired yet another boat capable of carrying sixteen cars. The Kessock Watch Committee, now in being, pronounced the boat too long for the piers, and in one final effort Mr Macdonald put a dredger to work on them.

Meantime, regular ferry users were refused season tickets for the motor boat in temporary use, and staged a sit-down protest within the boat. All good publicity, but better was to follow. In November 1938 the Watch Committee put their own boat, an open motor boat, on the ferry. Mr Macdonald raised an action in Dingwall Sheriff Court against Alex S. Patience and others to interdict them from so doing, and was successful. The Watch Committee responded by a complaint to the procurator fiscal of the Justice of the Peace Court in Dingwall, who prosecuted Mr Macdonald for failing in his duty to provide a service as required of him by statute. For six hours the hearing lasted, and in the end he was found guilty and fined £10.

Sir Murdoch Macdonald represented Inverness in Parliament, a Liberal with a majority of 816 in March 1922, and a Coalition Liberal with a majority of 1011 in November 1922, after which he became unassailable. A civil engineer by profession, Sir Murdoch had always been a supporter of the cause for a bridge across Kessock. In Ross-shire the sitting member was Mr Malcolm Macdonald, Socialist son of Prime Minister Ramsay Macdonald. He had despatched Mr Randolph Churchill at the polls. Both these M.P.'s with access to advice from the law officers of the Crown, informed their constituents that the local Authorities had power to acquire the ferry rights by compulsory purchase, and to provide the necessary services.

Discussions commenced between the relevant town and county councils, culminating in the formation of a joint committee to acquire the ferry rights. Negotiations were opened with the luckless Mr Macdonald, but as time was passing the watch committee hit hard by forcing the local authorities to compulsory purchase. Mr Macdonald had a right of appeal, but did not avail himself of it. We can imagine with what relief he was delivered from the whole sorry business when the local authorities took possession in November 1939.

By this time all concerned were involved in a much more serious conflagration, and the ferry was crowded out of the news.

The clip clop of the cabbie's horse is now but a distant echo in the minds of an ageing group of old Invernessians, as are the *Lowestoft Belle*, the bogie roll, and saga of the sunken armada of poor Mr Macdonald.

Dan Dallas

ONE THING above all others was admired by boys. Strength. Elmo Lincoln, King of the Jungle who appeared in a serial in the La Scala was watched regularly, but after all, he was but a silent shadow on a silvery screen. The boys of Inverness had a strong man of their own to worship. His name was Dan Dallas.

Dan Dallas was a small man, five feet five inches would take him in. He had huge shoulders, a deep chest, and bulging muscles at calves and biceps. He had the short springy step of the athlete, toes slightly turned out in his walk. A large nose sat on a clean shaven face, and a sparse brush of brown hair adorned his pate.

Through the years his dress never changed, brown boots always well polished, woollen stockings, brown tweed plus fours and jacket, brown tweed hat. He had a watch at his left wrist, a pocket watch (turneep) in each of his lower waistcoat pockets, and a stopwatch in one upper.

In his younger days he had established a private gymnasium in Hamilton Street, in which he sought to make a living out of physical culture, but it failed. He got the job of teaching "drill" in the local schools, although he was without any kind of paper qualifications. Probably none were to be had in these days, outside the services.

The feats of strength he performed were legendary. Local furniture removers were instructed to take a steel safe from the top floor of the Workmen's Club in Bridge Street. They admitted defeat because of bulk and size. For a bet, Dan carried it single-handed down two flights of stairs to the street below. In the Music Hall six men on a light wooden platform, were lowered on to his shoulders, and he supported them for a few seconds amidst thunderous applause.

There was a bit of unkind doggerel composed by an unknown, which ran –

Dallas' nose is long,
Dallas' nose is strong,
It'd be no disgrace to Dallas' face,
If half of his nose was gone.

He alone could be the announcer at sports gatherings in the capital, and this, it was said, because none other could fill the nose hole in the megaphone. Electronic amplification had not arrived. Dan revelled in athletic meetings, where his Punch-like figure was never absent and there his announcements were made to each of the four corners of the field. These were the rare occasions on which his usually solemn countenance was allowed to crack, and a beam from Dan radiated infectious bonhomie.

On a wet day his intimation might be followed by, "Utt's a graan day fer ducks."

Or when a big crowd was present, "Ah naavur saa a crood like thus sunce Mayraak's coo died."

He was also the starter, "On yurr maark. Redy. Gett sett," Bang, bang. A mouthful of invective was piled on the shoulders of the sinner who made the false start.

For years he was attached to a concert party of budding amateurs who played in Inverness and surrounding district for charity. Inevitably he was comedian. Though an indifferent singer, he had a number of gramophone records to his credit, like "The Bonny Black Isle," and "The Highlan' Rodds is Long, Long, Long, an' th' Highlan' Whusky Strong, Strong."

An annual event in Inverness was the musical play *Rob Roy*. There could be only one Dougal Crater − Dan Dallas, the faithful slave of Helen MacGregor. He had a personal verse in the theme song, which could only be his own −

Th' Dougal waas a rogg she waas,
Rob Roy, MacGregor-o.
The Dougal haas two durty paas,
Rob Roy MacGregor-o.
If you will be th' Dougal's friend
The Dougal he will surely lend
His erm, his durk; his life commend
To Rob Roy MacGregor-o.

When Erch and Andy first witnessed this classic annual, their interest was in one performer only, Dan Dallas. He never let them down. But there was an episode at the end of the saga which disappointed. Dougal bared his manly chest and invited Helen to plunge his dirk into it. The chest was innocent of hair.

Dan became responsible for the physique of all the boys in Inverness. Employed by the school board, he visited all the primary schools once a week. He also held sway for the secondary schools in the Academy gym. Dan and his bike were inseparable, and his compact figure, straddling the bike, was a familiar sight in the streets of town as he pursued his primary visits.

By present standards, his system may seem primitive, but it was essentially sound. Walking rather than marching.

"Keep yurr heid upp, an' yurr belly unn. Swung yurr erms."

He might pick out Duncan the Larkin (Leachkin) who had two left feet and two left arms.

"Waak beside me an' do utt like thus."

But Duncan always had to lift his feet high to clear the heather.

"Ach, yurr a propper ploochter."

There were bending and stretching exercises, Highland dance steps, and his great favourite – chest expansion. When he demonstrated chest expansion, in profile it was as though a huge bellows had been released inside him, and a great shelf arose under his chin. It caused a draft. Then there was netball. Netball was a great joy at drill, and he knew it. He often minimised drill to maximise netball, a wild and exciting game, the only trophies from which were bloody bruises.

In the gym there were climbing ropes for which the boys made a dash as soon as they got in. Always when he was ready to start there were boys up the ropes. The first order was "Gett off them ropps!"

If he was a disciplinarian, he could also be a philosopher, and would discourse briefly on what to eat, how much exercise to have, the need for a daily clean out, and the desirability of a day of rest, even if you were not a church goer.

"Th' old folks werna fools y' know."

Adam Tait was sent to Dan's brother's shop in Castle Street to collect his wrist watch which was at the mending. When Adam brought it back and handed it over, Dan observed that the little leather keep-strap, used to hold down the end of the wrist strap, was missing.

He pointed' "Wherr's thaat bittie?"

"Ah donno," said Adam.

"Ach," said Dan. "Th' next time ah send you f'r a messuge, ah'll no send y' att aal."

He was sparing with his praise. "No baad," was about as high as he would go.

He was also responsible for swimming instruction, and was on parade at the Montague Row Baths whenever the schools were there, although no-one had ever seen him in the water. After Erch got away with the breast stroke, he was swimming in five feet of water when Dan walked by.

He pointed down to Erch and said quietly, "Thaat's no baad."

The ultimate accolade.

He also gave dry land swimming instruction during drill periods in schools. One of his best was on floating.

"Eff y' waant t' flott, y' jist lie on yurr baak. Y' stretch oot y'r erms like thus. An' y' pitt yurr heid baak like thus. An' eff y'll jist do thaat, y'll flott f'r a week."

Everybody loved Dan.

Strength And Dare Do

ANDY AND Erch were playing cigarette cards against the stone mason's gate. The gate was close-boarded and five feet high. This was desirable to flick the cards against. The dwarf walls fronting the houses were too low. Of course they could have played in their own yards, against the house or against the coal shed, but that was for private. If you wanted at the same time to see what was going on, you played in the street.

Widow Shaw passed with her shopping basket, clothed all in black, yet she did not look an old woman. There were so many of them thanks to Kaiser Wilhelm. You could tell a real old one because she wore a mutch − a black concoction like a broad hoop over the head, secured by a black ribbon under the chin. The mutch was dressed with black lace and sequins.

A tribe of tinkers appeared. The tinkers had camps at Bunchrew, Dunain Croy, the Longman and Stoneyfield, depending on the clan. There was also a long established settlement on the canal banks, near the Sandy Braes. The matriarch was usually sent to do the begging, because she could speak the language best. The lingo was a mixture of English and Gaelic, which is difficult to understand. The tinkers had no respect for conventional education, and were constantly in trouble with the authorities for failing to send the children to school. The teachers did not mind, because the poor tinky child always stank. Little wonder. No-one could live in their primitive and overcrowded tented conditions, particularly in winter, and avoid the clothes reeking of wood smoke. Each clan had its own piper, whose pipebag required constant treatment with whisky to keep it in condition. At any rate, that was the story. The tinkers were rather menacing of demeanour, but they only fought when drunk, usually on feek, methylated spirit. In their fights they damaged each other, and the citizenry were seldom involved. Few of them were strangers to Porterfield Prison. Dire threats were made against the chemist who was reputed to be supplying them with feek, so long as they paid the price. But he was not breaking the law. The matriarch picked up some clothes and one or two ''pieces'' on her rounds, and the clan moved on.

''Ah'm fed up o' playeen kyards,'' said Erch.

''Me too,'' said Andy, ''Let's do sometheen else.''

They wandered into the mason's yard. They were quite accustomed to going in there to pick up small bits of sandstone, which they rubbed on harder stone to fashion them into various shapes, diamonds, hearts, or stars. They found Joe Wilson the mason in the yard, about to lift a large stone on to a little table with splayed legs. He started dressing the stone with a cold chisel and a mason's mallet.

He looked up when the boys approached and said ''Aye, aye.''

Both boys replied ''Aye aye.''

''Keep baak a but,'' said Joe. ''Un case y'll gett a chup in the eye.'' The boys retreated a little.

Andy asked, ''How heavy's thaat stone?''

''Ach utt's aboot a hunnerwate,'' said Joe.

They watched enraptured as he skillfully knocked off the rough edges to give six pretty, smooth, faces. They wandered to the far end of the yard out of Joe's sight, and had a competition to see who could lift the heaviest stone. There were hundreds of them and they soon tired of that.

''Joe sed that stone waas a hunnerwate,'' said Erch.

''That's notheen,'' said Andy, ''A bag o'coal is a hunnerwate.''

''Aye,'' said Erch, ''But Quail carries th' coal on his back. He doesn't luft utt from the ground.''

Recognising the truth of that statement Andy said, ''Wush ah cood luft a hunnerwate.''

Erch's mind was working. ''Look Andy, y' know the rings

they hev in the baths?''

"Aye," said Andy.

"Well, we cood have rings like them. T'any rate we cood have two in the coal shed. Let's go an' try t' mek them."

"What, evernow?"

"Aye."

They went to Erch's back yard and opened the coal shed door. Erch had a vision of himself swinging from ring to ring, nonchalantly, his muscles bulging, as the more skilful did in the baths. There was a timber lintel above the door, and another similar bearer four feet in, carrying the corrugated iron roof. It would be easy to slip a rope between the corrugations, one on each bearer, and swing from one to the other. But they could not find a rope. They went to their respective houses to look for string and returned with a bundle each. The first thing to do was to segregate the German string, which was made of brown paper rolled up. That was treated with contempt, just as on other occasions they had treated the German train on rails which irreparably broke down before it gave any fun. The Germans were sending over lots of clockwork toys which were trash, but were bought by harassed parents at Christmas because they were cheap. Maybe the Jerries were getting some of their own back. The selected strings were plaited three-fold, and three-fold again, and tied to the roof bearers, but when they tried to swing between, the string cut their hands, and anyway they could not get a grip. So they got bits of firewood and made handles. That was better. They were getting on fine when one handle slipped and Erch fell sprawling to the coal shed floor. Elbows and knees suffered, and they were too sore for secrecy. Jean washed the broken skin, and she bandaged the knees. Erch was rather proud of the knee bandages. They were like those worn by Bowden sometimes in the Caley goal.

The Old Man was told of the disaster, and he came to inspect.

"Ach, thaat's no good," he said. "Ah'll gett sometheen better."

Using fence wire and half-inch copper pipe for handles,

he rigged two "rings" which would never come down without the shed. As a refinement, he also fixed a length of one and a half inch cast iron pipe (just like the baths) across the coal shed door, at a height which required the boys to jump for it. They had fun with the new rings, but their affection was soon transferred to the "bar." The Old Man showed them how to pull themselves up to chin the bar, and how to turn somersaults. They also had their own game which was to last for long enough. Swing from the bar to maximum height of legs, and then let go to see who could project himself into the yard farthest.

This was great. They practised and practised. Then they selected certain of their mates to have a go. It was strange how stiff most of them were. None of them could equal the agility of Andy and Erch, and this gave great satisfaction. Their hands became brown and leathery with constant bar practice.

They went on to other things, all in the search for strength. Cartwheels and walking on hands. Andy was great at both, and left Erch standing.

Then it was a case of "Ah c'n do sometheen you can't do."

The paling between the yards was four feet six high, of open spars, pointed at the top. They vied with each other to see who could walk farthest along the top of the paling.

Andy said he would jump from the top of the coal shed – a six foot drop. They became quite good at that, and again the mates were invited to see and try for themselves. Few did. The thing to remember was to splay the knees on landing. A knee on the chin was no fun.

Then it was see who could run farthest with a gurd (hoop). A gurd was usually the rim of a bicycle wheel, propelled with a piece of firewood. They both went to Clachnaharry, one mile.

Then it was see who could climb highest on the trees in the school shrubbery. Quits.

Then it was high jump over a string stretched across the yard. This they enjoyed immensely.

Then it was keep uppity with a sorbo.

Then it was headacks with the same sorbo.

74

Then came the ploy to end all ploys. At the back of the boys' houses there was a lean-to enclosing the kitchens on the ground floor and the bathrooms on the first. The two small bathroom windows were level, and some fifteen feet from the ground.

"Bet y' won't drop fr'm the bathroom window" said Andy. Erch did not like the idea very much, but Andy was determined. He went to his bathroom, climbed out the window, hung from the sill for a moment, and dropped. He landed with a clatter on the ground and came up smiling.

"S'easy," he said, "Only a durl in the feet."

Erch was not persuaded. So Andy did it again.

"This is too much," thought Erch. He must do it too.

Off he went to his bathroom, out the window, and hung on the sill. He was afraid to let go, but there was no going back. He dropped, and forgot about the knees. Knee cracked on chin without doing serious damage, but that was the last time for him. Andy was quite cocky about this great feat, and did it several times more, until one day he dropped and left the bathroom door locked. There was a panic in the Andy household. If his Old Man came home and found what had happened, the belt would be out. Andy and Erch both tried to climb up the rainwater pipe which passed close by the window, but made nothing of it. There was great tension. Andy's Mum was as agitated as he was. Andy's elder brother Eck came home, and he too had a try. His boots slipped on the harled wall, and he made little progress. He tried again, wearing sandshoes, but no good. Then he tried barefooted, and with an effort born of dire forebodings of the consequence of failure, he made it.

That finished "dare-do".

Tents And Fullums

THERE ALWAYS was plenty of evidence of the British Army in Inverness. The Seaforths were at Fort George, and the Camerons were at the Hut o' Health. The Terriers had the Rose Street Drill Hall for the Camerons, The Margaret Street Drill Hall for the Artillery, and the Strothers Lane Hall for the Lovat Scouts. The other two services were little known or seen. Small Naval craft occasionally came into the canal or the harbour, and when the Fleet was at Invergordon, the impact was felt in Inverness.

From the beginning of recorded history Inverness was the meeting place of warring factions, and accustomed to strife. It was always palpably vulnerable, and there always seemed to be someone around showing strength. King Brude chose Craig Phadrig for his fortress, the ruins of which can still be traced on the hill which also guards the Giant's chair. King Duncan chose, we believe, the Auldcastle Road area for his castle. Shakespeare, through the mouth of Duncan, said of it, "This castle hath a pleasant seat; the air nimbly and sweetly recommends itself unto our gentle senses." But finally the strong point was located on a sand hill, to overlook the four routes which met at the River Ness, by the ford or bridge, the site of the present castle. The first edition was erected by Malcolm Canmore in 1057, and ten years later he granted the burgh its first charter. Shaw MacDuff, son of the third Earl of Fife and of the Royal Family, took the name of Mackintosh, and became the first recorded keeper of the castle.

Inverness must therefore always have been a town accustomed to warriors and bloodshed, right down to the last battle on British soil at Culloden in 1746, after which the rebelling Jacobites were pursued into the streets of the town and were slaughtered. Then the town was huddled below

76

the castle for protection, and comprised dwellings and places of business only on the two banks of the river, downstream from the present Ness Bridge, King Street, and the North Road (Young Street, Tomnahurich Street, and Fairfield Lane), the Kirk Street, High Street, and Petty Street, and the Old Edinburgh Road (Castle Street).

So at the time of our narrative, sojers, or swaddies, were a familiar sight in the town and the populace were sympathetically disposed.

The urchins were interested. Camping was a fascinating military activity which captured the imagination.

It was only natural therefore that Erch and Andy, at some stage in their advancement to maturity, should want a tent. The fence between their respective yards was a starting point. Rakes, brush handles, shovels, and spades were propped up against the fence crisscross. These were clothed with bags – coal, potato and cinder. So could a primitive shelter be created by improvisation, with the materials at hand.

The thrill was more in the building than in the use, although a cup of tea and some scones could be taken out and they could pretend they were living in the tent like sojers. They then had the idea of interior lighting by candles. The candles were made from scrapings from the household candlesticks, kneaded in the palms, and rolled into a thin tube, through which a piece of string was passed. There were two snags. When the rain came, they might as well have been in the open, for all the protection the bags gave. Secondly, the interior was not dark enough for the candlelight to be effective.

So there was another idea. Build the tent in the coal shed. The shed was cleared of all the muck a coal shed-cum-general purpose building contained, and the tent was built as before, over half the space of the coal shed. There were risks involved. A false move could bring down the flat of a spade on the nut. But that was part of the fun. A tent in the coal shed was dry, and the candlelight satisfactorily effective.

Light was transferred from one candle to the other by

using a spill of paper. A spill of paper was like a cigarette, and it was a short step to experiment with paper cigarettes. Both Andy and Erch achieved the great art of blowing smoke through their noses, and this had to be demonstrated to others in the street, who had not attained any expertise in the interesting new found art. It was another short step to pinching ''doubts,'' (cigarette ends) from fathers and older brothers to have a go at the real thing. This was purely imitative – a passing phase which never became addictive. ''Doubts'' were not easily come by, and paper led more to sea sickness than addiction.

The next idea was to hold concerts in the coal shed, giving rise to practice on the buzzer (comb and tissue), mouth organ (moothack) and tin whistle. Poems and Scots songs were also popular.

The following were among the poetic gems: –

Get into bed said sleepy head,
Time enough said slow.
Put on the pot said greedy guts
and we'll feast before we go.

The boy stood on the burning deck,
His feet were full of blisters,
He couldn't put on his own trousers
So he put on his sister's.

It was a dark November night,
A man stood on the street,
His weary eyes were full of tears,
and his boots were full of feet.

Chewing gum, chewing gum, put me to my grave,
My mother told me not to eat it but I disobeyed.

I love a sassage, a bonny German sassage
I got a sassage for my tea.
I went to the cellar to fetch my umbrellar
And the sassage came after me.

Half a pound of tuppeny rice, half a pound of treacle
That's the way the money goes, POP goes the weasel.

When it's Springtime in the Model,
The Model in Chapel Street,
The fleas begin to Yodel,
And the Trampies canna sleep.
They go and light a candle,
To wash their sweaty feet,
When it's Springtime in the Model,
The Model in Chapel Street.

The other street boys were not prepared to spend money to see a show in a coal shed. The satisfaction of their curiosity was worth, however, a marble or a button. Some expressed enthusiasm, but more, contempt.

Angus Urquhart (Angie Urk) heard of the concerts, and Angie Urk had a magic lantern. Like most cheap toys it was a product of Germany. If any toy deserved the description of jerrybuilt, this was it. It was a black tin box, five inches by five inches and standing six inches high. It had a lum at the top which curved like a shinty stick. At the back was a wee door through which was inserted the illumination, a wee paraffin lamp with an opaque white globe. To the front was a little, two-glass lens. A piece of wire stood up from the box turned to a right angle at the top. On the horizontal bit of the wire hung the film, which was fed in between the light and lens upside down. A handle on the right of the box wound the film through, a frame at a time. The feed-in had to ensure the turn of the handle projected the frames truly.

The result was a moving picture about the size of a postcard, but real moving pictures, albeit they were jerky and not all that clear because the light was so poor. But nobody could deny, whatever their quality, they were moving pictures. Above all else Erch and Andy coveted that magic lantern. They reviewed their treasures. Meccano parts, marbles, a catapult, a penknife (one blade broken) and a pocket watch that did not go. An approach was made to Angie Urk, offering the meccano parts, in which they knew he was interested, but they were not enough. He stripped them of their all before they possessed that wonderful magic lantern. Then they ran their own shows.

But although they used an electric torch instead of the paraffin lamp, the batteries for the torch were a problem. They required money. They invited the Old Man to see the show – hoping. He was most interested, and said he would make a better light for them. He constructed a gas works, using two large, round biscuit tins, one eight inches diameter by twelve deep, the other slightly smaller. One was upended inside the other, and the lower one contained a quantity of water. Carbide, which was not expensive, went into the water, and the gas given off caused the inside tin to rise, gas filled. A rubber lead was taken from this to a bicycle lamp jet, and that inside the lantern gave a superb light. This gave much joy, and the two went into the highways and byways to barter for more film. Willie Strachan was their best bet. His father was a projectionist in the Central Hall, the cinema in Academy Street. Willie got good cuttings from his father and he sold them cheap. He even got a bit showing Charlie Chaplin.

Invited guests were privileged to see their selection of films in the tent in the coal shed – at least till Fred Fraser came. They always thought he was a groick. He had to take cramp, sitting as he was on his haunches, behind the great new toy. He stretched himself suddenly and involuntarily to his full height, crashed his head on the roof of the tent, and brought down a shower of spades, rakes, shovels and bags, all on top of the magic lantern. The film strayed across the naked light, and the whole shed was immediately a mass of smoke and flame. The management and audience escaped unscathed and roused the neighbours to their aid. Soon a willing band of adults were flinging buckets of water on the conflagration. The shed was saved, its wooden framework only charred. The films, the magic lantern, most of the bags, and one or two handles were completely destroyed.

Erch could not very well be blamed when one of the root causes of the fire was a naked flame designed by the Old Man. So, there was no disciplinary action.

Other avenues to excitement would now have to be opened.

Education

SCHOOL BECAME real and earnest at the age of seven. First thing in the morning was "Our Father." Then there was the ceremony of bringing out "Black Jack" – the strap. The strap was kept in the cupboard, and when the class was in session, occupied a privileged position at the front of the teacher's desk. The teachers called it a "Lochgelly," the principal supplier being a saddler from that airt. He must by now have passed over. Wonder whether he was well received?

The system of teaching was largely based on homework. Every night twenty spellings from a wee book one and a half inches broad and twelve inches long. More than three errors in the morning, and one of the strap on the palm for each one in excess. Six to ten sums, and one of the strap for each wrong in excess of three.

There was quite an incentive to have no mistakes.

At the week ends, composition or nature notes, and strap at the teacher's discretion, depending on the view taken on results.

Poetry and Bible to memorise, and again the strap for deficiencies. Any hope of engendering a love for poetry or the Bible was destroyed for many.

Sometimes there was a conscientious objection on the part of a teacher to using the strap for Bible delinquents. An alternative punishment could be even more sadistic – stand in the corner before the class, and be pointed out as examples of ungodliness to whomsoever should enter the room.

These, at any rate, were the tactics of some teachers. There were others, bless them, more enlightened, who lived in the minds and hearts of their pupils all the days of their lives. Teachers who taught, teachers who lived and read and knew about the world, teachers who imparted real learning, and had no interest in creating deferential parrots, obsequious to sanctimonious whims.

There were certain definite advantages to be gained from a father in the right occupation, who went to the right church, and who helped to keep the class's end up with contributions to the Penny Savings Bank, the pass book of which was endorsed with the words, "Take care of the pennies, and the pounds will take care of themselves." Such fathers also imposed rigorous discipline in the matter of homework. Every section of society has its snobs, its élite, and its downtrodden.

Supervising the whole, was a headmaster who was a war veteran, who was manly, who was a disciplinarian, who was feared, and who was respected.

There were highlights of school life. Dan Dallas was one.

Lewis J. Owen was another – he supervised "singing." He toured the primary schools like Dan Dallas, and took several classes together in the hall for singing. He did his best to keep discipline. The smaller ones sat on small forms at the front; the older ones sat on higher forms further back; the still older ones stood on the floor, and the seniors stood on forms at the back. The recognised good singers were pulled out to the flanks. In all it was a large mob to control. A teacher played the piano. Owen would conduct, or start a song and walk around. Ewen Yule was capering at the wrong time. As a senior, he was standing on a form at the very back, and Owen caught him red-handed. He clenched his fist and planted it in the small of Ewen's back, sending him flying over the floor standers, to land sprawling among the middle-seat sitters. He surfaced with the grin wiped off his face.

It is probably true to say that Lewis J. Owen's pupils learned of his value in after life, when they realised the fund of knowledge they possessed of Scottish, English, Welsh, and Irish airs, together with folk music of other countries, enriched with an introduction to many of the classics.

THE SCHOOL
CHOIR

He applied for, and missed, the job of Director of Singing to the Education Authority of Edinburgh in 1920, at a salary of £500. However, at about the same time he became conductor of the Inverness Choral Society against strong competition. His impact on Inverness was not carved in stone, but even now there are those who acknowledge the heritage of song derived from sitting under Owen – singing.

To the boys the most important function of the Janny was to instruct the tolling of the bell, an office for which there was much demand. He allocated this task as fairly as possible, and in a very quiet and friendly way he tried to maintain discipline in the playground.

Inspectors visited occasionally. They put the teachers in much more of a dither than the pupils.

Members of the School Board prowled around from time to time, and there could be few scholars who did not know Black Joseph Macleod, so called because of his black beard. A Sutherland man and popular, tea merchant, and Liberal agent for Sir Murdoch Macdonald, Joseph was known to say, ''I know all the boys in this town, but I find it difficult sometimes to remember their names.''

The minister called for the Bible exam. There were no brickbats from him, but if the performance was not up to the expected standard there was hell to pay when he departed.

Inevitably there were temperance lectures when a gentleman came to address the whole school. He put a worm in a glass of whisky and it died, no-one was told what happened to the whisky. There were prizes to be won for temperance essays, and plenty of ''Pale Ale'' pencils with which to write them.

Photographs were taken of the class, many to be hoarded and give infinite pleasure in adult life.

There were cultural visits to the Theatre Royal on Bank Street, to see *Macbeth* or other classics, completely over the heads of primary pupils. But in their own time they went gleefully to see ''Ned Carter the Railway King,'' on film in the Central Hall.

Sports Day was much the same as in any other school,

84

sometimes held on the hallowed turf of the Northern Meeting Park, sometimes in the public park in Bruce Gardens, sometimes in the Caley Park. The Sports Champion always elected to take a football for his prize, and the headmaster always said of him – how considerate, a real sportsman, to share his winnings with his mates.

Then there was a Closing Day, when Mrs Glass denuded her rose bushes so that all could have a flower to stick in the jersey. Black Joseph often presided at the presentation of prizes, and the pupils sang for the delectation of parents.

Sometimes there were finger inspections for the boys, to trace smokers and punish them. On such an occasion the head was very doubtful of Andy and Erch. The insides of the fingers were discoloured, but the conventional signs were not there. Further investigation was called for.

"Do you smoke?"

"No sir."

"What are these marks on your hands?"

"Don't know, sir."

"Is it tobacco?"

"No sir." He would not understand the "bar" so there was no use explaining.

"Did you used to smoke?"

"Yes, sir." Pause. "I used to smoke my brother's doubts." Titter from the class.

This sounded very close to insubordination, "Floor."

Erch and Andy trooped out to the floor and took three on each hand. The head had an expert action. He did not follow through with his stroke, but brought the handle of his Lochgelly sharply up as the other end was falling. This had a whiplash effect. Expectantly the class waited to see the victims double up in pain. Not so. Thanks to the "bar" the pain which got through the leathery hands was minimal, and they came up smiling.

There were visits to the school doctor and the nurse. The nurse was primarily interested in finding "nits." A nitty one was sent home and the parents advised on treatment. Measles and whooping cough were commonplace, and ringworm sometimes appeared. Willie Jack was fortunate,

85

or unfortunate, to take ringworm. His head was shaved and he wore a large bonnet both indoors and out. Few boys ever wore headgear, so the bonnet was the envy of many, and Willie was delighted to doff it to show off his bald head.

There were fights and a fight was a great institution. When two had a difference of opinion, the dark challenge went out, "See y' at four." The formal fight was after school closed in the afternoon and the teachers had departed. The Janny kept out of the way.

The word went round like wildfire, "Fight th' day."

And the question was, "Who's fighteen?"

A large audience could always be depended upon and they formed a circle round the contestants, and sent up the piping chant "Fight, fight." The protagonists made no preparation. They faced up as they were, in jerseys, boots and bare fists. There was little display of technique, there were no rounds – the fight simply went on and on and without any referee. There was an unwritten law which said that as soon as blood was spilt the elders among the crowd would stop the fight. If at that stage no-one had emerged as the winner, there might be another challenge.

Booties was not an aggressive type. His nick name came from the very heavy ironwork on the soles of his boots, soles meant to last. His father was an amateur gardener who produced massive blooms of all kinds. Booties' jersey usually bore a centrepiece of floral art. His nose was also a bit leaky, so the bloom might well be greasy. In a knockabout football game in the playground before going into class after "denner," Booties had an altercation with Leslie, equally inoffensive. Booties alleged that not only did Leslie knock off his chrysanthemum, but he also kicked him on the shins. Leslie wore galluses or braces to keep up his trousers – braces of a kind all too common at the time. They were inclined to roll into a tight cylinder, so that they were difficult to keep on the shoulders. It became almost an involuntary action on the part of Leslie to hitch up his gallusses by upward rotations of his shoulders. The motion was such that it could be indicative of another form of discomfort, so he became known as "Lousy Les", a nickname accorded without offensive intent, and borne by Les with some pride.

"See y' at four," said Booties through glowering black eyes. They met, and there were crowds of witnesses. They were well matched, and the fight went on without blood. It was a great fight and the two fought to exhaustion. They both had blue marks about the eyes, but there was no blood, until, at last, Leslie made a lunge which caught Booties on the lips. A trickle of blood came from Booties mouth and from Leslie's knuckles, which had also connected with a strong set of teeth. The fight stopped.

The sequel to a fight of this intensity should have been eternal enmity. It was not. These two became inseparable friends to the end, when they died together as privates, in the Camerons, in France in 1940.

Big Bess

BESS, without her high heels, a *sine qua non* of the age, stood about five foot six. However, in conversation she held her head back, looked down her nose, and gave the impression she was much taller. Her shoes were plain, her stockings were plain, the tweed suit was plain, the summer blouse and the winter jumper were plain, and the black, bobbed hair was plain. Sartorially, Bess did little to enhance her appearance.

But the face, the face, that was different. Triangular it was, isosceles, the base at the top. A broad brow, which, if it had any depth, was camouflaged by a fringe of black hair. On either side of the well-shaped nose, the cheeks fell down to the chin, narrow, and delicately rounded. The mouth was framed by straight lips, not too thin, and on special occasions accentuated by a modest application of lipstick, in a time when a deep, greasy red was *à la mode*. The skin was without colour, a pallid white to which cosmetics were unknown. The eyebrows were very black, the lower lids straight lines, with the upper forming semi circles above. The lashes were nondescript, and there was no make-up in this region. It was the eyes which were compelling – grey, or black, or brown, who could say? You could say they were cold, cynical, searching, superior, grave, threatening. They expressed her knowledge, her capacity, her competence, her whole being – with just a little held back.

"Stand still!" said Bess. The voice was the command of the Archangel chastising Satan. She cast a baleful eye over the cowering load of riff-raff it was her misfortune to indoctrinate and endure for a whole year. She allocated seats – four rows of girls to her left, four of boys to her right.

"This," she said, rummaging in her table drawer where at last she found a black object, "is the strap. If we get on well, no-one will see it again. But woe betide any mortal who crosses me."

The strap was unceremoniously stuffed back into the drawer, never to be seen again.

The scene was set as carefully and as eloquently as for any melodrama, and the director knew exactly how she wanted the production to proceed.

Former teachers had crammed into the thick protesting heads great screeds of Genesis – In the beginning God created the heaven and the earth; Samuel – Saul and Jonathan were lovely and pleasant in their lives; Proverbs – Vanity of vanities . . . and the Shorter Catechism – what is the misery of that estate where into man fell?

Hap, hap, happy holydays.

Bess could not keep her job and ignore the Bible altogether, but her object was not to get the bairns to spout interminable and incomprehensible screeds from the Good Book at the Bible exam, conducted by the school parson, and so earn his approbation. Her tactics were simply to tell the stories of the Bible, to make them live, to be remembered. When she came to a dirty bit, she apologised, and said the class was too young to understand that bit.

There was no preferential treatment for the headmaster's son, the son of the grocer from whom she got her weekly order, or those who went twice to church on Sunday. The sons and daughters of toil had an equal but no better chance with Bess.

Her contemptuous retort to any non-answer was "Balderdash!"

"What is the capital of Wales?"

"Newcastle, mam."

"Balderdash!"

Nick names came readily at our school, and she could well have become Miss Balderdash. But a nickname, especially one of ridicule, would not sit easily on Bess' head. By personality alone, Bess avoided becoming Miss Balderdash.

She made a point of appearing at most of the school football matches, a silent spectator, but she was there. Her presence was sufficient encouragement to greater endeavour. Never was dignity sacrificed to emotional self-expression.

Regularly on Saturday evenings she attended the Theatre Royal, where her preferred place was in the dress circle. Her tastes were catholic – it could be Shakespeare on the one hand, or Dr Walford Bodie on the other. Bodie claimed to pass unbelievable currents of electricity through his body, and caused great flashes of lightning to impress, and to accentuate, his stress. As the act concluded he was carried off in a fainting (?) condition. A great fraud but great showman. Then he hypnotised members (?) of the audience, and made them look ever so stupid. Bess loved this and suffered imperturbably the sweetie papers aimed at her from the Gods. Donnie Dickson wondered why the following Monday he was put through the mill by Bess without any reference to the theatre. He did not know about her protective Gestapo.

One of the pearls of wisdom she imparted was that some of the swear words in current use were quite respectable in bygone times. The use of swear words in that environment visited the wrath of the headmaster, and as night follows day, the strap.

Bess said she had once been to a circus where there was a very funny clown whom she quoted – "I thirst for blood. Therefore, bring me a BLOODY pudding."

With this most of the boys were delighted, but inevitably reports of Bess' transgression went back to horrified parents – even to elders in the church. The headmaster was approached, but truth to tell, Bess was too formidable a dish for him to handle, and if any chastisement was administered, it was minimal. Anyway Bess did not give a damn, and most of the boys were on her side.

Angie Urk was caught passing a note to his enemy Davie Mac. Bess insisted on seeing it.

It read, "You are a dirty b---r."

Bess pointed to the last word and said "Should be two g's."

Around Christmas time there was snow on the ground. Bess was well placed right in front of the open coal fire.

While the rest were starving, at least her bum was warm. Willie Wordie in the back seat had a need. He often had a need – that's why he was called "Willie Widdles." It really was not his fault he was "needeen." He did his best with a weak bladder. He put his hands, palms out, between his thighs to stifle any involuntary flow. The need persisted, and in desperation he raised his hand and snapped his fingers for the attention of a preoccupied Bess.

"Please mam, leave the room?"

"Certainly not boy. Get on with your work." Dismayed, but not surprised, Willie replaced his hands in the "stop" position, but things got worse. Soon he was bouncing up and down in his agony, faster, faster. At last he subsided with a sigh, and a thin column of vapour rose into the cold air.

Commotion in the back seat. His mates ostentatiously drew as far away from him as they could, quite unable to suppress their sniggers. The boys in front turned round to see what they were missing, and even the attention of the girls was drawn. Bess became alive to the stir, and, gliding like a ship in full sail to the back seat, took in the situation at a glance.

With no emotion she said quietly, "Willie, go home."

Willie retreated swiftly, eyes on the ground.

In the morning interval Willie's bladderdash could be clearly traced on the route of his retreat through the snow.

The hubbub subsided and the class reassembled. But there was new excitement. The cause was the drawing on the blackboard.

Bess was quick to spot the misdemeanour.

"Who, pray, is responsible for this?" said she pointing to the board. No answer. The menace in her voice, her whole demeanour was communicated to the class.

"Right, we shall soon find out." She started at the front seat of boys, questioning each individually.

"No, mam."

"No, mam."

No answer.

"No, mam."

When she came to Ian Mackay in the back seat, ''Yes mam.'' Bess exploded.

''Get out to the floor and wipe that board clean.''

Nothing could be heard but the pit pat of Ian's little feet, as with one stocking down, jersey all rumpled, tie askew, dossan over right eye, and ashen countenance, he made his way to his allotted task. The lace of his right boot was loose. He trod upon it with his left, and went flying on the floor. This was usually good for a laugh, but not in this electric atmosphere. Ian picked himself up, unable to suppress the trickle of a tear down his pallid face.

Ian scrubbed the board. Bess contemplated the sinner, fists clenched, while the class awaited the next outburst, and then meet punishment.

It was not to be. Bess exhaled, relaxed, and collapsed in helpless laughter into her chair.

Never there scenes of such unrestrained disorder in Bess' class, and probably never did it occur again.

The illustration on the blackboard was that of a dripping tap!

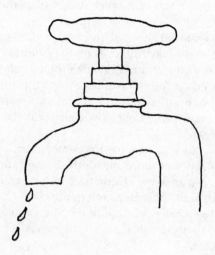

Sa'urday

SOMETIMES there was no programme for a Saturday. The day just had to evolve.

There were always messages – the butcher's for mince, a bit steak for the Sunday dinner, perhaps a bit of boiling beef for the soup, or a bone. At other times in the butcher's, there was the great occasion when he would provide a sheep's head. This was taken to the smith's to be singed, after which it was boiled and boiled, and the result was potted head, sweet as honey. After boiling, the eyes of the sheep were much sought after, they were so tasty. As an alternative to sheep's head there was always hoch, which made potted meat with much less bother than a sheep's head. The other main messages of the week were to the grocer's for lentils or split peas for the soup, barley for the broth, semolina or sago for the pudding, sugar for the tea, oatmeal, good and coarse for the porridge and oatcakes, flour for the girdle scones, tattie scones, and pancakes. There was always a concourse of wifies in the grocer's shop, because the grocer was a member of the Brethren, and spent more time in his overcrowded shop preaching than making up orders. His shop was a bore, but this was mitigated by the fact that he knew where all his produce came from, and that was an education. His writing was quite indecipherable to everybody but himself.

From all these shops bowshers operated, (say "bow" as in "cow"). The more humble traders sent the bowsher out with a great, square basket on the arm, and the more prosperous with a basket on a bike. As a luckpenny, bonus, or free gift, however you like to look at it, there was usually included in the basket for free, a poke of batchelor's buttons (pan drops), rose buds, or other similar boiling.

93

All the bowshers were great whistlers, and the tunes of the moment reverberated round the streets, as in Italy the most humble citizens sing merrily the choruses from the great operas. Every boy could whistle. Every journey was a journey of whistling. The streets were alive with the sound of music, which could be rated from talented to putrid. Away from the music of the whistle to the call of the whistle. The most mournful was the "come back home" call to a missing dog – a miserable "Toot, toot, toot," through pursed lips. There were those who emulated the shepherd, using the fingers, either the thumb and forefinger of one hand, or the first and middle fingers of each hand inserted between the front teeth, to give a penetrating wail, to draw attention, or to summon back any dog at any distance.

After the conventional messages had been attended to, Erch was assigned to take his boots to the shoemaker for repair. Andy went with him. Fraquhar on Young Street was a boys' man, and a cobbler with a philosophy.

When he saw the boots he said, "Good Goad, wha' ha' y' been doeen wi' them, keekeen tuns?"

"Aye," said Erch.

"Well y'll hev t' stopp keekeen tuns or ah'm no goeen t' mend y'r boots f'r y'." He turned them over and looked at the soles. He noted the wear, the outsides of the heels, and the toe points.

He remarked grudgingly, "No baad wear."

"What y' mean uts no baad wear?" asked Erch.

"Well," said Farquhar, "Y' c'n tell the sort o' fella who wears th' boots by th' way the soles are worn. That kind o' wear is th' wear of a sensible kind a fella. Eff th' wear is on th' outsides of th' heels, th' soles, an' th' toes, y' know th' fella is bandy legged. Mebbe a good athlete, but he hasn't gott much upstairs. Eff y' waatch how a fella waaks, y' c'n tell whaat kind o' mind he's gott. Eff he goes ovuur on th' baak o' th' heel an' th' tip o' th' toe, he's a countryman, he's always waakeen on rough ground, an' he probably knows the ways o' nature. You waatch, just waatch, how peeple waak. Th' fella who's gott knock knees thaat hit each other wi' every stepp, is a very shy character. Th' fella who waaks wi' his toes turned out an' his body erect is probably an aggressive character. Th' fella who's knees describe a semi-circle unwards, us no aal ther. Jist you waatch. Y' c'n tell th' peeple's character fr'm th' way they waak.''

Erch and Andy took all this in, and went their way, leaving the boots at Farquhar's mercy.

"Let's hev a gemme o' durbs," said Andy. They both had their marbles with them, in little cloth bags hitched to their braces where they met the front buttons.

"Follow me dedd," said Erch, and they got down to the gutter, throwing their durbs across Huntly Street, on to the Suspension Bridge. Half-way across Erch's durb fell through a drain hole, and that was the end of that game.

"Let's go t' th' Round House 'n Millburn Rodd t' see th' engines," said Andy.

They crossed the bridge, through the wee arch for pedestrians. They paid a visit to the mine, the underground urinal at the east end of the bridge, to relieve themselves. They sensed the pungent smell of spirits at Mackintosh's Queen Mary's House at the corner of Bridge Street and Bank Street, past Melville's Boot Shop, and Macdonald the Ironmonger, past Gellion's Hotel, and the Steeple tobacconist, across Church Street, past Mackenzie the Chemist, and the Bank of Scotland with its beautiful stone carvings. Past MacDougall's tweed warehouse, and Mayor's Drugs, the chemist with the large golden mortar and pestle above the door, Mackay the Booksellers, Grant's Close and the Northern Hotel, the British Linen Bank, Jackson the Shoe Merchants; Mealmarket Close, Dickson the Brassfounder, and Forbes the Draper. Over to Eastgate, and past the Clydesdale Bank, Hamilton's Marts, and the Lochgorm Inn. In the high wall, which separated the railway property from the street, there was a wicket gate which they found open, and in they went to the round shed. There was a hive of industry there, with a dozen men or more clustered round the gleaming form of a steam locomotive. The railwaymen had little time for small boys. Permitted they were to watch at long range, but they were not to be taken into the confidence of these master craftsmen, who were dealing with dangerous machinery, from which small boys should keep a fair distance. With nobody to tell them what was going on the boys turned back on their tracks. On the opposite side of the street this time, past the Plough Inn, across Crown Road and Stephen's Brae, past Macrae the Jeweller, and on again to the High Street. Past the Old Post Office Buildings, Howden's the Nurserymen, Dr. Helen Macdonald's, Macdonald and Mackintosh of coffee fame, at whose door the exotic odour proclaimed their specialisation in the coffee trade. Past Campbell the Draper, The Clan Tartan at the corner of Castle Street, with the stone figures of Faith, Hope and Charity looking down from above. Past the Victoriana which is the Inverness Town Hall, on to Castle Wynd, with a look up to the fire station with its polished engine, Jack the Exchange Grocer, Mackenzie the Tobacconist topping Bridge Street, Junor the Licensed Grocer, Bernardi the Confectioner with his fellow countryman Rizza two doors down, My Coat's All Wool the Clothier, the Workmen's Club, Carrie the Grocer, County Hotel, and back to the suspension bridge.

Time had passed and they wandered down by Tanner's Lane towards the cathedral, where they found Oag the Warden cutting the grass with a hand mower, two long ropes attached to it being pulled by small boys. It was worth watching. The rope-boys soon became tired, and offered Andy and Erch a go. Erch and Andy were happy to have a go because they had never cut grass before. The reward for cutting the grass in front of the cathedral was the honour of ringing the bells. This meant climbing the cathedral tower into the belfry.

Those who were experienced at the console could chime out, ''Come to church and hear the sermon,'' which command has syllables equal in number to the notes in the octave of the bells.

The others, like Andy and Erch, were only allowed to toll. This became quite an interesting diversion – help Oag to cut the grass, and enjoy the distinction of pulling the bells. This went on for long enough, until Eck 'Pherson, who had a

A STROLL ON THE
"EXCHANGE"

very good ear for music, paid the price of cutting the grass, and was allowed into the belfry. He was not content with "Come to church and hear the sermon." He played on the bells for all the populace to hear, "Show me the way to go home."

That was the end of that ploy. Provost Mackenzie, the senior cleric, imposed a discipline which prevented a recurrence.

Torvean, The Sandies, And The Diviner

THE HOLIDAYS were becoming a bit of a bore. There had been lots of rain, which kept Andy and Erch at home or, at best, in the shed.

But after St. Swithin's six weeks of rain there came a fine day of sunshine.

They set off to walk with a piece in the pocket. They intended to have their picnic at the memorial which occupies an elevated position above Clachnaharry, and looks out over the Beauly and Inverness Firths and across to the Black Isle. The memorial marks the site of a battle between Clan Chattan and the Munros in 1333. It was Chattan's custom to levy tax on all cattle beasts of plunder which passed through their territory. The Munros failed to meet their dues, and were pursued to Clachnaharry, where the two clans met. Chattan was routed and their chief killed. On the way the two would have a drink at Duff's Well at Muirtown, earlier known as the Anointing Well, believed to have been used by the Druids, who lived on the hill above. The Earl of Montrose while being conveyed a prisoner from Sutherland supped at this well also.

But their plan was not to be. When they reached Muirtown Road Bridge over the canal, the bridge was open to allow a ring net herring drifter to pass to the west, its noisy Kelvin engine chugging away on two cylinders, half the block, as these engines could so effectively do on canal passage. The fishermen swore by the Kelvin, which they kept chugging away from the moment they left harbour to the moment they returned from the fishing grounds a week later. The boys followed the *Mary Ann* from Buckie, to the locks.

99

Canal staff always seemed to the fishermen, forever in a hurry to make their passage, thin on the ground, and crew were put ashore to help with the opening and closing of lock gates. The long poles were inserted into the slots in the bollards on either side of the canal, and on the boys' side only one man was leaning his full weight on a pole to open the gate on his side.

"Wull y' nae gie me a hon?" said the Buckie man to the boys, in his strong eastern tongue. They did not understand.

"Whaat?" said Erch.

The fisherman pointed to the pole opposite him and unmanned, and said "Heeve." This was understood.

The two boys manned the pole and helped to wind their half lock gate to the open position. The drifter moved slowly into the lock.

When the boat rose to wharf level at the top lock, the Skipper, who was aware he had helpers, said "Like a scudd?"

"Yus please," replied the boys in unison.

They were handed on board by a crewman. This was fine. The idle anglers on the banks along the reach drew in their worms as the boat passed. The boys waved, important-like, and the landlubbers waved back. The surface was smooth as glass and the water clean as a spring. Where else is there canal water fit to drink? Several citizens were enjoying their walks on the banks on either side, some with dogs, and some with prams. A few cattle grazed disinterested. The greenery of the banks was at its best, and the delicate dog roses nodded approvingly. Midway to Tomnahurich Road Bridge the Skipper sounded off, and the boys all but jumped out of their skins. Reluctantly they landed at Tomnahurich Bridge, delighted with their first experience of being at sea. The *Mary Ann* went on her way as Telford planned, to Dochgarroch Locks, Loch Ness, Fort Augustus, Loch Oich, Loch Lochy, Banavie Locks, Corran Narrows, the Sound of Mull, and then the fishing grounds off Barra. Mallaig would be their home port while the fishing lasted.

Tomnahurich was a long way from Clachnaharry. The

two reviewed their plan and decided to climb Torvean (Torravayunn in the dialect) instead. This heap of sand, also left by the retreating ice, was a happy hunting ground for boys. Through a field next to Loch na Sanais, they went to the foot of the hill, over the stile, and on to the well defined path which led to the shoulder, through the birches and the rowan, the whin and the broom, chasing every rabbit which appeared before them, and disturbing the sonsy Cheviots which grazed happily on the rich turf. The top was some five hundred feet, and a narrow plateau extended to the Dochfour boundary. They looked down on the canal and the river side-by-side on their left and the hills of Strathnairn beyond, while on their right was the road to the west, with Craig Dunain and Craig Phadrig beyond. Every now and then the trees and bushes retreated to allow the walker to enjoy a pleasant glade. They sat on a great concrete slab in such a glade to eat their pieces. It was a gun emplacement from which no shot had ever been fired in anger. At the Dochfour march they disturbed a roe deer which loped gracefully from sight, distrustful as he was of human kind.

The same thought was in both minds. The Sandy Braes. They had examined the Sandies in passing, and they made their way back to that point. The Sandies rose from the canalside at a varying angle of up to sixty degrees. The slope was of loose sand, rubble, stones, probably created by careless pick and shovel quarrying at the foot, over a long number of years. Alex Ross brought his horse and cart almost daily along the canal banks to claim the fine rich sand of Torvean Hill. He had a ready market among the builders, for concrete was coming.

How often had they been asked, "Ever been down the Sandies?"

Till now they always had to answer "No."

Andy went first, and chose his way carefully. Back to the hill, and sliding more on his rear than on his feet, he caused a cascade of sand to precede him, and to follow. Loose stones too were dislodged, and these constituted a danger. A clout on the nut from a boulder would mean curtains. Whenever the boots got a grip he changed direction to right

101

THE "SANDY BRAES"

or to left to find an easier passage, keeping his head up from the sand as much as possible for fear of following boulders. At the bottom he shouted to his mate "C'm oan!"

Erch made the same passage using the same techniques. Comparing notes, they both had sore elbows and bums.

"Look!" said Erch, and bellowed a great gust of laughter.

"Whaat?" said Andy, seeing no reason for such gaiety.

"Y've no seat un y'r pants." Andy felt where it mattered. There was a hole worn on each cheek.

"Lemme see yours," said Andy. Erch turned round and it was Andy's turn to laugh. Likewise Erch had no seat in his pants.

They stretched their jerseys groundwards as far as they could to hide their shame, and turned for home.

The tinkers were brewing up as they passed their camp, and a mongrel dog challenged them, barking. They stood still till he was called off by a raucous shout from a man in a muffler, and then went on their way, looking back every now and then to make sure they were not being followed.

When they got to the Loch na Sanais field there were two men like farm workers walking towards them from the middle of the field, one behind the other, the big one in front, and the wee one behind. The leader was holding his hands in front of him as though riding a bicycle. This looked so daft they stopped to watch. Every now and then the wee fellow would stick a greenstick peg in the ground, and on they would go, slowly, in an erratic way. As they came closer they saw Mr. Big was holding a forked stick, one horn in each hand and the point directed straight ahead. When they came to the fence they stopped. One pipe was lit and one cigarette. Mr Big's eye lit on the boys.

Through the pipe-free side of his mouth he said – "Waatcheen?"

"Aye," said Erch. "We were waatcheen. Whaat y' doeen?"

"Dowseen."

"Whaat's dowseen?"

"Ut's caalled dowseen or divineen, lookeen f'r waater – dranes. C'm oan, an' ah'll show y' how."

There was a barb on top of the fence, and the two boys slipped through two lower strands into the field. Mr Big, kindly disposed, put the forked stick, eighteen inches long into Andy's hands.

"That's hazel," he said.

The instructions were palms up, elbows to sides, grip one horn of the fork tightly in each hand, and walk slowly forward. Andy did this and nothing happened. Then Mr Big faced Andy holding his wrists, walking backwards as Andy walked forward.

"Feel anything?"

"Yus," said Andy excited. Though the twig was held firmly in his hands, the point was turning downwards to the earth.

"Water down ther," said Mr Big, "But y' hanna gott th' guft."

He handed the twig to Erch, and told him to walk. Almost immediately the point started to rise.

"Is thaat rite?" said Erch.

"Aye," said Mr Big. "Sometimes up, sometimes doon."

The twig went horizontal.

"Y'r off utt – a butt t' th' rite." Erch moved a little to the right and up went the point again. Within a few minutes he was able to walk with the point constantly in the up position, and, in fact, led by the hazel, he walked in a straight line between two of the green pegs.

"Aye. Y' gott th' guft aal rite," said Mr Big.

By the time they got home they were so excited about the dowsing they forgot about their pants, and they had so much to tell, that, discipline-wise, the matter was closed.

Too Few And Too Many

"AH'M OFF t' th' Thaatcher's," said the Old Man to Jean.

He was of a generation which grew up before football became popular. Football, which interested so many at that time, held no interest for him, and shinty somehow passed him over also. There was only one bowling green, which, being club owned, was rather exclusive. He had two extramural activities, the plot and the Thaatcher's.

During the First War there was a Dig for Victory Campaign as there was in the Second. As few had gardens sufficiently large to produce vegetables, the town arranged for land to be made available for just that purpose. There were areas on Glenurquhart Road and on Fairfield Road, divided into sections called plots. The plots were let out to any willing to make a contribution to the war effort by growing. Many of these plots continued in use for years after the war – until inevitably, they gave way to building development. The Old Man grew his spuds, cabbages, and turnips without enthusiasm, affording them the minimum attention required for cropping.

The Thaatcher's was a different proposition. It was a run down but and ben, condemned as a residence, and let to the Old Man at a modest rent as a hobby workshop. He stripped off the ancient thatch and replaced it with corrugated iron. He knocked down the dividing walls, to make one large compartment, with the original flagstone floors. There was a small yard at the back, adjacent to Jackson the Dyeworks, and on the lane right opposite there was a communal water pump to serve the whole lane. Such water pumps were scattered about the older parts of the town – a cast-iron, cylindrical stand, fifteen inches in diameter and three feet high, capped with a cast-iron cover with a spout, all in the shape of a lion's head. It was operated by turning a handle like a door-knob, just below the head, and the water spouted from the lion's mouth. When the handle was released the flow was automatically turned off.

On the same lane was the ''broken housie,'' the remains of a fair-sized house which had been burnt down many years before, and left in ruins. The timber work had been plundered, and the stones had been so well washed over the years by rain, that they were quite free from signs of burning. The broken housie was of course a magnet for boys, for there it was possible to build castles or housies, or what you will, in real stone without the supervision inevitable in the mason's yard. Whatever was built was as vulnerable as the castles in the river.

The Thaatcher's was equipped with a bench, a vice, and a miscellany of tools – hammers, chisels, pliers, files, screwdrivers, saws, picks, and shovels.

The Thaatcher's was a place where couthy cronies met. There was no imbibing there, but the *Ordnance* and the *Tarry Ile* were not far distant.

The cronies used the facilities of the Thaatcher's for cutting their firewood, and setting up any jobs requiring to be done for their own homes.

But that was all incidental to the yarning. The local and national scenes were kept under constant review. There was little divergence of political opinion for almost all, whipped by the *Inverness Courier*, were staunch supporters of Murdoch Macdonald, the Liberal M.P. for the constituency, the local boy who had made good.

Sandy the Thatcher was a regular at these meetings. He was a small, old man with a powerful frame, a broad face with laughing eyes, and a bonnet. Nobody ever saw him without his bonnet, so that his hair, if any, cannot be described, but his moustache was grey and bushy. Moustaches in older men were more the rule than the exception. He smoked a black, short pipe, silver or tin, mounted at the joint. He smoked bogie roll – black twist.

Anybody who smoked black twist successfully – to be judged by the use of no more than six matches to a fill, and the expression of complete contentment in the smoke – was an artist. In preparation for a smoke, the pipe was placed in the right corner of the mouth, and a roll of tobacco from a dirty pouch carefully sliced into the palm of the left hand with a pocket knife. It was a matter of pride that the knife was kept razor sharp, and the Old Man kept an oil stone for the purpose. A spit was used more than oil. The roll was then returned to the pouch, and the pouch to pocket. Then the slices were rubbed with loving care and great precision, until Sandy was quite satisfied the preparation was adequate. The makings were then gathered together skilfully to the hollow of the left palm, the pipe removed from the mouth and placed in the "ready to fill" position. The dottel from the last smoke was then prized from the bowl of the pipe with the knife, to join the virgin makings. Both were mixed together with the point of the knife, and all coaxed into the bowl, again with the knife. The knife was then discarded, and the forefinger of the right hand continued the packing operation. The last shreds were filled in by bringing the palm to the upright, allowing them to fall to their target. The bowl was carefully and gently packed with the right forefinger, the pipe being rotated the while. The consistency within the bowl required to be just right to meet the standard of the artist. The ritualistic part of the operation completed, a match was applied. The first match was only a primer, but a really talented performer got the pipe going with the second, and then the wee tin lid with the holes in it was clamped on top of the bowl. There were those who maintained combustion with endless matches, but they were to be frowned upon.

The Thatcher complained of too few, and John the Plub complained of too many.

The Thatcher mourned the coming of corrugated iron from Clydeside, and slates from Ballahulish. These cold, ugly, modern contraptions were replacing the beautiful thatched roofs in which he specialised, havens through the years for bugs and bayonets. He pointed to thatched roofs in the lane alongside corrugated iron and slates and said:

"Uts obveeous whuch us th' best, b't peeple jist can't see. Ah wuddn't sleep undurr eye-urn nor slets f'r anytheen. W'd you John?"

John was a tall man, also strongly built, solemn of countenance, cleanshaven, and unlike most of his friends he wore a trilby hat, albeit somewhat battered. He had his pipe going too. They were sitting side-by-side on a plank supported by two dressed stones from the broken housie.

The question required some contemplation, the kind of contemplation which exasperates the non-pipe smoker. John gave one or two pulls at his pipe, and a pull on twist has to be strong, and each ejection of smoke was preceded by a "Phutt, phutt, phutt," from the lips as they opened to exhale.

At last John was ready to pronounce.

"Thaatch us dam durty. Coreegated an' slets us faar be'er, an' faar cheeper."

"Ach," said Sandy. "Y'r jist dam thraan. Ut's becos o' peeple like you a'm un a dyeen tred."

John was called "the Plub," because his employers were the town council, and his job was to keep the urinals in the town clean. A urinal was called a "Plub," or a "Plubbie." His complaint was that there were too many. Daily he could be seen tramping round the plubs, long brush and mop under his arm.

"Ah hev t' go T' Brooce Gairdeens," he said, "t' Wells Street, an' th' Carse, th' Maggut Green, Plenfield Rodd, th' Gregg Street Brudge, th' mines un Bank Street an' Ungls Street, Eest Gett, th' Castle Stepps. Ut's faar too meny."

He paused to attend to the twist. You only have to miss a puff or two and the damn thing needs more matches.

He continued: "Thank Goad th' Coongil don't thunk leddies leak, orr ther w'd be a dam sight moar."

True, there was no provision for the needs of "leddies" but he wasn't finished.

"Dudd y' heer whaat thaat stupeed sochulust Smuth sed a' th' Park Waard meeteen laast nite? Fine coonsullur he'd mek. Sumbudy esked hum, 'C'n we no hev a urynaal aat

108

Glenurchart Rodd?' He sed, 'Uff y' eelect me ah'll see ther us nott oanly a urynaal 'n Glenurchart Rodd, but an arsenaal aas well.'''

There was a movement in and out of cronies, almost like a pub. Andrew the Smith, Hugh the Post, Malkie the Milk, and sometimes Kenny the Mash. At five o'clock they thinned out, as the gates of the *Ordnance* and the *Tarry Ile* opened.

One of the regular visitors was MacColl the Architect. The Old Man and he were very friendly. Together they were experimenting at the Thaatcher's with the construction of interlocking concrete blocks for building construction. They were ahead of their time, and perhaps just missed the boat.

Erch came in from the broken housie. The Old Man saw he was looking uncomfortable.

"Whaat's wrong boy? Needeen?"

"Aye, ah'm needeen," said Erch.

"Whaat," said the Old Man, "Lochies or jobbies?"

"Jobbies," said Erch.

The Old Man put a broad shovel flat on the slab floor, and stood a twelve inch cutting of a six inch drain pipe on top. He handed Erch the front page of the *Courier*.

"Ther y'aar, gett onn w' ut."

When Erch performed, the proceeds were removed to the yard to be buried in a prepared hole.

Northern Meeting Time

A THLETICS played a big part in the life of the youth of the town, starting with school sports, graduating through inter-school sports, to adult gatherings organised by the Amateur Athletic Association. The Athletic Association held at least one meeting in the year, for which the Northern Meeting Park was made available. Events included flat racing up to one mile, high jump, throwing the hammer, putting the shot, and cycle racing. It could not be said the town was overflowing with candidates to participate in these competitions, but there were usually sufficient to make it worthwhile.

The devil who so often struck was the weather. A wet night and a lot of money went down the drain.

The "Daddy" of all gatherings was organised by the Northern Meeting, a private voluntary organisation whose members were primarily landed gentlemen.

The Northern Meeting Games were held in the Northern Meeting Park, eventually sold to the town council after the abandonment of the games following the Second World War. Rising costs tolled the knell for this outstanding gathering.

The time was mid-September, conker time, when every boy had a chestnut on a string, and a dozen in his pockets as spares. Conker time was a time for raiding the chestnut trees, mostly mature amenity trees in the streets. Kenneth Street, Ness Walk, and Ness Bank were a picture, lined as they were with grand old trees which were not replaced after felling, lest the roots would lift the hallowed new fangled tarmac. Stones or sticks were directed at the fruits to fetch them down. The best of them were hardened in the oven in the hope they would become unchallengable conquerors. But, for the Northern Meeting, conkers were discarded.

The importance of the event was marked by the award of two half holidays on Thursday and Friday when the games were held. Anything which warranted release from school was of some significance. There was a distinctly festive air about the town. The games were professional, and attracted the big names in athletics from all over Scotland. The Heavies were the centre of attention for the urchins, representing as they did manly strength. Often the Games coincided with the autumn manoeuvres of the Home Fleet based on Invergordon, and Naval contingents of athletes enlivened the scene. On occasion they brought with them their Marine Band to perform in the streets and in the Park, to contrast with the pipes and drums of the regiments from Cameron Barracks and Fort George.

The Games were held in the middle of the Highland "Season" when all the shooting lodges, leased to the new rich by the impoverished lairds, were filled with guests. It was a time of maximum traffic at the station, a time when the public school accents of the Highland lairds mixed incongruously with those of first generation English industrialists.

From all the outlying areas crowds of visitors flocked into the town, and the shopkeepers and publicans rubbed their hands with glee.

There were no bookmakers.

Each afternoon of the Games the park was full. Ardross Street was lined with locals to watch the movement of distinguished members and their guests to and from the members' enclosure. Kilts were everywhere. Sometimes Royalty were present – all the more reason to stand and stare.

Even Harry Lauder's kilt was there on one occasion. He was giving a very bad-natured performance at the Central Hall, by then the Empire Theatre on Academy Street. Dan Mackenzie, a loyal doorkeeper at the members' entrance refused him admission – he being a non-member and not the guest of a member. There was hell to pay, as anyone would understand who knew the kind of temper Lauder tried to hide behind his more accepted public image. The situation was saved by the arrival on the scene of the secretary with the requisite apologies, and a grant of the freedom of the enclosure. Lauder left Inverness after that visit not liking it very much, and the feeling was mutual.

In the park there were two large stands. One still exists, and was the prerogative of members. One at the west end was later acquired by Thistle Football Club, and still serves at Kingsmills. Lesser mortals had timber slatted stands, erected by the games contractors Messrs A. and D. Smith the local joiners, both of whom in later life became town councillors.

The committee of the Northern Meeting were purists so far as matters Highland were concerned. They would countenance the wearing of the kilt only by men. Kilted girl dancers were banned, but as we all know so well, in this sphere the traditionalists have been scuttled. The athletes in the heavy events were all obliged to wear kilts. All the member officials on the field wore kilts, as did most men in the members' enclosure. Most of their ladies wore tartan long skirts with suitable silver adornments. Track and heavy events, piping and dancing all went on at the same time. The officials might include Lord Lovat, Lochiel, Mackintosh of Mackintosh, Capt Kemble of Laggan, Lord Cawdor, Lord Macdonald of Sleat, Sir Reginald Macleod of Macleod. The clans represented included Chisholms, MacPhersons, MacBeans, McQueens, Grants, MacGillivrays, MacTavishes, Macleans, Cummings, Brodies, Andersons, Munros, Mackays, Mackenzies, Stewarts, MacDougalls, MacGregors, Maclennans, MacRaes. Could there today be an occasion of such glamour?

The Games were the backcloth for the premier piping competitions in Scotland, the arrangements for which are still the voluntary obligation of the Northern Meeting, but now held indoors. The sound of the pipes was therefore constant – tuning against the boundary wall, competing before the solemn faced judges, accompanying the dancers, or displaying in the band. The pipes took second place only to the Marines, resplendent in their pith helmets and red tunics.

There were marquees from which refreshments could be obtained – hard or soft.

The picture was set in a framework of greenery – the trees on Ardross Street, the cathedral grounds, and Bishop Eden's garden. The massive, but kindly, structure of the cathedral looked down upon the scene also, a little aloof but not disapprovingly, reflecting the beauties of nature in its manmade elegance.

The kilts, the plaids, the dresses of the ladies, all played a part in adding to the colour of a spectacle which radiated festivity, gaiety, anticipation and relaxation.

All that happened on the field of play was announced to the four corners of the park by megaphone, in the hands of Dan Dallas.

In the evenings, after both games, when darkness fell, the ladies of the town were in attendance in Church Street, to view the dresses of the dancers going to the Northern Meeting Ball in the elegant purpose built rooms. Below that roof there was the most dramatic array of colour of the year, and Mrs David Logan played as she alone knew how, for the reels and country dances. No other could be entrusted with the responsibility of so grand an occasion.

But back to the Games. The charge for admission was one shilling, minimum. Erch's and Andy's total wealth came to nil. They had abandoned all hope of seeing the heavies for there was no dodging through a gate. The guard was too strong. There was no sympathy as at the Caley Park, and they had no bargaining power. On Tomnahurich Street they met Johnny Bottles. Small, unshaven, tramp-like, copious overcoat, and the inevitable sack over his shoulders from which came the clink of bottles. Usually Johnny was not a conversationalist. On this occasion it looked as though he, too, was celebrating.

"A've cum fr'm Abriachan," he said, "Wi' a good brew. Ah'll be a wealthy man th' nite."

He ripped a cork out of a dirty bottle and extended it for

113

THE "NORTHERN MEETINGS"
NOT WITHOUT
DAN DALLAS AND HIS
MEGAPHONE.

the boys' delectation. They declined. He said it came from the ''bonnyiest wee stull un aal Sco'land.''

''Uff y'se waant t' go unta th' gems – unta th' Hostul Paark, ovur th' Bushop's Waal, then ovur th' Meeteen waal. S'easy. S'long.''

He staggered on his way.

''Heer whaat he sed?'' asked Andy.

''Aye,'' said Erch. ''Let's have a look.

They went in to the hostel grounds where there was a gentleman flying a kite carrying a streamer advertising the *Daily Mail*. He had one or two urchins as spectators. The hostel accommodated Academy girls from the outback of the county, and is now part of Highland Regional Buildings. The two went over to Baino's workshop which ran parallel to the Bishop's wall and about three feet out. Baino was the handyman for the schools. The wall was eight feet high but the stones were uneven, and it was as easy as pie to climb over. In the Bishop's garden they found the apple trees heavy with fruit. They filled their pockets, it was such a temptation. Then they approached the Northern Meeting wall, at right angles to the other. That was just as easy. Over they went and dropped down into the park. Ex-Sergeant Major Ewan MacPherson of the Cameron Highlanders was on guard within, clad in tweed plus fours and cap, and wearing a white armband of office above the left elbow. It was a fair cop and they fell into his arms. Through their minds flashed visions of the kind of punishment which would fit their heinous crime, aggravated by pockets full of apples. MacPherson hustled them behind a hessian screen which served as a make-shift urinal.

''Stoap ther tull ah tell yuh,'' said MacPherson.

They stood there shivering with fright, wishing the heavens would open and envelop them.

A few minutes later MacPherson reappeared and said: ''Aal rite boys, c'm out now, but f'r Goad's sake git loast un th' crowd.''

There were two small boys, their pockets filled with apples, in the expensive enclosure among the hoity toities. It was too much. They made their way to the barrier of the bob enclosure, and dodged under the fence. Not even officialdom could complain about transfers from the expensive to the cheap area. They felt safe among their own kind, wormed their way to the front of the crowd, and yelled their heads off for the heavies.

Granny Watson

IN A CELTIC community there were those to be found who possessed powers or skills which could not be explained by the ordinary application of reason.

The phrase "second sight," was frequently heard, and those to whom it was applied enjoyed a pleasing kind of notoriety. There were those who dreamed or merely sensed the future, and by giving utterance to their hopes or forebodings, became personalities in their own right. Most such were unlettered, and could give no explanation of their powers, if such they may be called.

There were charlatans who read cards for money, and were never completely inhibited by prosecution. It was generally thought, however, that the possessors of genuine second sight could not turn on the power at the drop of a hat. The revelations came to them whence they could not tell, and indeed they were often alarmed that they should be the vehicles through which the veil before the future was lifted.

There was in Inverness, and throughout the Highlands, a more or less harmless practice of reading fortunes from the leaves of a tea cup drained of its liquid. The origin of this activity could not have been of long standing, since tea was not introduced before the middle of the eighteenth century. Some readers were more proficient than others, in consequence of which they acquired a certain aura of respect from their fellows. "Reading the cups," was almost exclusive to the fair sex.

"There is a ship here. You are going to take a journey over water. I see a bird on the wing. You will be getting news of an old friend you haven't heard from for a long time. There is a great deal of small stuff here. You will be getting a lot of money . . . I see no tears. It is a good cup.''

A young one might hear:

''There is a dark man crossing your path and he is putting a proposal to you. I can see wedding bells not far away.''

Some of the cup readers began to believe what they read. Some, who found tragedy in a cup, abandoned the practice, convinced the future was better left a mystery. In the main a light-hearted activity, but, when touching the imponderables, best left alone.

The healers were in a different category, and among these, much sought after, were the bonesetters. Anyone can try bonesetting, but few have the confidence, and fewer still the gift, for that it must be called. Then, as now, the doctors frequently referred patients to the bonesetter. The effect of the work of the bonesetter was immediately to be seen and felt. The really successful were few, and their services much in demand. They were not permitted by law to charge fees. In the main bonesetters were dedicated, and sought no reward.

Granny Watson was born in Cromarty. She was the widow of a line fisherman, and saw the village bonesetter at work as a young girl. When the cailleach died, she fell heir both to her talents and her responsibilities. Granny Watson stood less than five feet high in her widow's weeds, and her mutch sat on her head well tilted forward. Her face was deeply wrinkled with the cares of her many years, but the grey eyes were bright, and the smile was ready, to reveal a mouth of uneven teeth. She was quiet and gentle in everything she did. She had a loathing for only one thing – strong drink, which she regarded as the instrument of the devil. The only scathing words that passed her lips were directed to drink. In her walk she leaned forward as though straining against a wind, and, there being no wind, the impression given was that each little foot was thrust ahead just in time to prevent her overbalancing. She was completely illiterate, never having been to school. She signed her pension form (the pension being her only form of support) with the aid of a neighbour who wrote ''Jessie Watson,'' and below, ''Her mark." Granny Watson put her cross between the words "Jessie," and "Watson."

Andy and Erch were fooling about with a ball in the school playground after hours. Erch had the ball at his feet and Andy was behind. Andy gave his friend a playful push in the back, and Erch tripped over the ball, falling awkwardly to the unyielding hard surface. He got up to continue as before, but felt a sharp pain in his right shoulder. The right arm was immobilised and he felt sick. At home Jean undid the neck buttons of his jersey to have a look. What she saw she recognised – a dislocated collar bone.

"This is a job for Granny Watson," she said. "Off you go."

Erch and Granny Watson were already firm friends, and she gave him a quiet welcome when he arrived at the little, dark house at 25 Upper Kessock Street, no longer standing. There was a small peep of fire in the grate, a kettle on the hob, and a small teapot stewing alongside. The room was poorly and sparsely furnished, but clean. A big paraffin lamp stood on the dresser, the only artificial light of which the humble two-roomer boasted. From the centre of the low ceiling hung a sticky fly paper which had already claimed numerous victims. A few flies were in flight to be shooed from time to time as they alighted on forbidden territory.

Calm as ever, the old lady took a look at the white face and said, "Whaat's th' maa'er, Sonny?"

"Ah fell an' hurt ma shouldur," said Erch.

"We'll jist sutt doon an' we'll ha' a cup o' tea before we look."

She sat him down by the fire and brought out two cups which she sugared and milked. She also brought out a quarter bannock of oat cake, which she broke in two and buttered. A black brew was poured from the sooty tea pot. She was unaware that a hundred years before the magistrates had condemned the use of tea as the "destroyer of the health and morals of the people." She put Erch's tea on a chair by his left side, and he felt most awkward using his k'yarack (left hand). They drank and they munched in silence. She noted the right shoulder, held high, and the

119

right arm across the chest, but no questions were asked.

Tea finished, she cleared away the cups and stood him before the small window to get the benefit of such light as found its way in. Gently she eased off the jersey, shirt, and semmit, and peered at the area of pain. There had been considerable swelling since last exposed. All she said was "Aye," but that conveyed many things to Erch. It meant she sympathised, she understood, and she knew what to do. So she should. Many the bruiser had been brought to this little old lady suffering from all kinds of dislocations of all the joints of the limbs. But this was a wean, with only a dislocated collar bone – child's play for her. But in doing this job she could not inflict too much pain. She got out the butter dish and put a small knob of butter on a saucer. Then she rolled up her sleeves and washed her hands. I am not at the point of reporting a spectacular result. That was not the way she worked. To re-locate the bone when the area was so swollen would have meant excruciating pain. She took a pinch of butter in her fingers, and began gently to massage around the affected part. Gently, gently, unhurried, methodically, and with infinite patience she weaved patterns on the skin.

For thirty minutes the work went on, until she said, "Thaa'll do f'r t'day." And that was just the start.

There came from that old woman, that ignorant, illiterate, an aura of complete competence and confidence. Erch was inspired with absolute faith in her ministrations. He went home with his arm in a sling made from his neck tie.

For five days she kept on with the gentle fingers, soothing, probing, round and round, up and down, in and out. At the end of the fifth day's work she stood behind him and said "Redy." She pressed, and the bone clicked back into place with little more than a pin prick.

Granny Watson had many appreciative letters from those she had treated, from football and shinty clubs, and she could not read one of them.

Dossans And Quiffs

IT WAS recognised that during the first few years of life the hair could be tended by mums. Mums, in the main, went in for long hair, the idea no doubt being to put off acceptance that the offspring was growing up. Sometimes the mums dressed the hair with some delicacy, sometimes they simply hacked, and sometimes they used the bowl method. By placing a "bow-el" of the requisite size on the head a straight cut could be achieved back and front.

The boys of the long hair complained for two reasons. The first was that it was effeminate. To be called a "Jessie" with reason was just the last straw. The unwritten code was, there must be no resemblance to or truck with girls. The second was that it gave too good a grip in a fight.

There were only two styles of hair cuts or "clups", one called a dossan and the other a quiff. The dossan involved a cut almost to the bone, with a small cheeky tuft left above the brow. The quiff was short back and sides with sufficient left to allow a parting.

Erch and Andy became conscious about the same time of the need to take this momentous step towards manhood. The adventure required to be parent-sponsored, since the cost was "tuppence." The fathers of both were sympathetic for obvious reasons, and the objections of the mums were soon overcome by pressure tactics. Consents were given, however, only on the basis of quiffs, not dossans.

Chaperoned by the Old Man, and with two pence safely hidden in trouser pockets, they made for Clarkie the Barber on Church Street. The Old Man made them and their requirements known to Clarkie, and left them to his mercy, charging them not to disgrace the family.

121

This was a new and strange environment. There was a man on the chair with a large bib around him. It was once white. Clarkie, who had grown old in the "tred," was in waistcoat and shirt sleeves pounding away at him with the hand clippers, then a new invention – the precursors of the present electric job. Operated with a scissors action, they reduced the growth to the required length much quicker than the old scissors could.

The shaving process was more interesting – the funny face covered with lather, and the scrape, scrape of the open-hand razor, sounding like a walk through dead leaves. Then there was always the chance of the hand slipping, and blood, and excitement, and angry voices. But it never happened.

"Whaat's th' sope f'r," whispered Erch to Andy.

"Ach," said Andy, "Ut's only so thaat the Barbur knows the buts still t' do."

Apart from the two boys, there were four other men waiting. Saturday was a busy morning. Clarkie had not tumbled to charging boys extra on Saturday to keep them away.

The adult talk in the shop was on two topics – football and toon cooncil. When football held the stage, the boys lugged in for all they were worth, and as they were in a Caley stronghold, they heard nothing with which they could take issue. There was only one team in Clarkie's, and that was that. When talk came round to town council, it was boring.

To pass the time the boys examined their surroundings. The floor was covered with hair of all the morning clips, short bits, long bits, brown bits, black bits, fair bits and gray bits. Clarkie was so busy he could not find time to brush it all up. Interspersed with the hair around the operating chair were little heaps of cigarette ash, for Clarkie had a lighted cigarette in his mouth at all times. There was a display shelf on which stood a few sticks of shaving soap, shaving brushes, combs, and small tins of brilliantine – hard as suet. On a lower shelf were the maestro's varied clippers, scissors, and combs, in an untidy mess.

On the form opposite, three of the patient patients were

122

"DOSSANS & QUIFFS"

clutching the *Highland News* or the *Daily Record*, while the fourth was holding a lead attached to a spaniel dog, on all fours below the seat. The spaniel had raised an enquiring eye when the boys came in, but showed no interest. Above the men's heads were coat pegs on which hung four caps – cloth caps, ceps, or bonnets – the weekday uniform headgear of the adult.

The "bo-nut," as now, had a peak which encircled the brow, and a cloth crown secured by a press stud, brim centre. The method of wearing differed, and to some extent revealed the personality. The conventional was straight brim, stud fixed, with crown slightly tilted to the left. It was a sign of gallantry to exaggerate the tilt. The man about town wore the brim on the skew, which together with the crown tilt gave a jaunty appearance. The fish men and the hawkers had the brim at a good forty-five degrees with the crown tilted as well, so that the cap just balanced and no more. The boys from the farms had a straight brim, the stud undone, and the crown pulled back. Come the motor bikes, and the cap was turned back to front.

The hour of waiting was becoming rather wearying when at last Andy was called. The operating chair was changed for a high stool. The "white" bib was folded in two and wrapped round his neck, tight as a hangman's noose.

"Good horreed," said Clarkie. "Whaat a heid o' hair."

The first operation was with scissors and comb, and Andy felt Clarkie's knuckles crack on the back of his head. He thought he had done something wrong, and that this was chastisement.

Clarkie said, not unkindly, "When ah hut y'r ther, y' tult y'r heid like thaat."

Then he put both his hands on top of the head and bent it forward. He then demonstrated the knock on the brow, the right temple, the left temple, the right side, and the left side. This formality completed it was knock back, knock front, knock left, knock right and the head went in the correct direction with alacrity. So military did the reactions become that one of the waiting newcomers let out a guffaw and chortled:

"He'd mek a graan sojer."

The signalling system enabled Clarkie to follow and participate in the conversation without interruptions which orders would involve. The clippers were the worst of it. To get a cut without inflicting pain it is necessary to follow through each stroke before lifting. A lift before a follow through results in a tuft being pulled out by the roots. There was a bit of squirming because of this, but at last the job was done. A clart of evil smelling brilliantine was administered, a roadie was formed to the left of the skull top, and the hair parted to either side. Tuppence was proudly handed over. Erch went through the same experience also parting with his tuppence, and they both went out to freedom.

They had a good look in the sweetie shop window adjoining to examine and admire their reflections, and felt quite the men.

They swaggered their way through the market entry to the fish market where the open-eyed cod seemed lost in admiration. A good business was being done at the three open stalls, but the boys did not like the smell. In the main market again all stalls were open – butchers and green grocers being best represented. In the Queensgate Arcade, John Young, second hand bookseller, had a display of books in racks in front of the shop, but they had little interest in books.

They wandered to the Academy Street Arcade, where, to their minds, the best display was in a jeweller's window. They gazed in wonder but without envy at the watches on show. One costing five bob (shillings) had a second hand representing Felix the cat who always kept on walking according to the song. Felix was bobbing up and down just as though walking. This they thought good fun. In the middle of their glee the shopkeeper appeared in the doorway, small, pot bellied, black moustache drooping, gold rimmed spectacles low on a hooked nose, and across his greasy waistcoat a heavy gold chain (known locally as a "yok") from which dangled a jewelled pendant.

In a Middle Eastern accent with Inverness overtones he said:

"Wot youse boys doeen heer? Eff y' vant t' vy a vatch, vy a vatch. Eff y' don't vant t' vy a vatch don't vy a vaatch, bot deep y'r durty noses off my vindow. Let th' vatches see th' peeple and th' peeple see th' vaatches. How d' y' think th' vaatches c'n see th' peeple, an' th' peeple see th' vaatches vith your durty noses against my vindow?"

There was no question he had a point, so the boys moved off. Kenny the Mash could have said it all in two words – "Scachter boys." He didn't believe in blethers.

Two more visits had to be made – MacPherson's Sporting Stores, Nirvana, and Toy Walker's Shop, Valhalla. These two shops, both in Inglis Street, contained all the heart's unattainable desires.

Och well, the cat can look at the queen.

The Po-leece

ERCH GAVE his face its Saturday morning wash and retreated to the bedroom where he pulled on his jersey and laced up his boots. He scraped his quiff to one side before the small mirror, and decided on the face he was to wear. He thought he might be a policeman. He flattened his feet and slightly bent his arms at the elbows. He hunched his shoulders a little, and turned down the corners of his mouth. The mirror said he looked the part. Anybody would know he was a policeman.

By the time he had his porridge he forgot he was a policeman, and went to greet the day – himself.

He met Andy returning from Mirtle the Bakers, a loaf under his oxter. It was wrapped up in tissue paper and still steaming.

"Aye, aye, Erch," said Andy.

"Aye, aye," said Erch, "How y' dooen?"

"Och y'r seen ut," said Andy.

That was an adult form of exchange carefully copied.

"Gem o' football?" said Andy.

"Don't mind," said Erch. "Ah'll get ma sorbo. Hev to be in th' street. Waasheen out at th' baak."

They kicked the ball to and fro with little enthusiasm. Andy was doing Sanny Docherty footwork as on the Caley wing. Erch was doing Blyth the left back.

Neil Nags Mackay (because his father was a cabbie) the bowsher for Jack the Exchange (grocer and wine merchant) had been delivering on Fairfield Road, and was returning to base on his bike, the basket empty. He rounded the corner of the street just as a strong shot beat Erch and went stotting in the path of the bike. Tempted, Neil jumped off his bike,

127

and let fly with a right foot, one which served the Haugh so well in the juvenile league. The sorbo flew straight for Aitken's window and through.

There was something ever so final about the clatter of glass. In the high pitched screech of its breech, and in the lower octave of its fall to the ground, it accuses. Lying helpless and useless in its conversion from the whole vertical, to the splintered horizontal, it expresses a mortal injury to the edifice which it served. The dark gap which its demise reveals, appears vastly larger than a foot rule would suggest. For those attending the death, there is guilt, direct or vicarious.

The two players had no time to think. Three things happened simultaneously. Neil jumped on his bike and shot like an arrow down the street, and out of sight. Mrs Aitken came to her door, furious, with the ball in her hand, and Davie Ross, a brand new boy of a Bobby, ambled round the corner, to take in the scene at a glance.

"Ah hopp y'll do sumtheen about thus," fumed Mrs Aitken. "Ah'm fed up w' them boys an' ther footbaal."

Davie took the ball from Mrs Aitken and held it up in front of the boys.

"Thaat your baal?"

"Aye," said Erch and Andy in unison.

"Right," said Davie, producing a notebook. "Thaat's aal ah waant t' know. Whaat's y'r nems?"

The boys gave their names. Davie carefully inscribed their names and addresses in his book, and returned it to his breast pocket.

"Y'll heer more o' thus."

As Davie made to depart, Mrs Aitken fumed "Ah hopp y'll pit a stopp t' thus nonsense waance an' f'r aal."

"Wheest," said Davie, "Ah'll do whaat ah hev t' do."

Davie went on his way, and Mrs A., a smirk of injury-cum-satisfaction on her face, gave a pout, turned her back on the boys, and slammed her door in their faces.

Everything happened so quickly, the boys were for a minute speechless. Then at last Andy blurted out:

"Neil Nag's a sneak."

"Aye," said Erch. "B't we canna clype."

To clype was to defect from the code.

The next two or three days were days of great unease and foreboding.

On the fourth day, the boys each came home from school to meet an enraged parent.

To each house had been delivered, by Davie Ross, a bit of blue paper. Part of it was written and part typed or printed:

The Complaint of John MacNaughton, Chief Constable of the Royal Burgh of Inverness. Andrew MacDougall, 7 Balfair Street, and Archibald Macrae, 9 Balfair Street, both of Inverness, YOU ARE CHARGED that, while acting in concert you did on the   day of June, 19   at 4.30 p.m. cause a ball of an unburstable type to be projected in such a way as to cause it to break a window in the residence of Henry Aitken at 10 Balfair Street, Inverness, and so did cause a nuisance, contrary to the Burgh Police (Scotland) Act 1892. John MacNaughton, Chief Constable.

On the back was a wee bit which said "Andrew MacDougall and Archibald Macrae, designed in the fore-_ going complaint. You are required to answer thereto in the Burgh Police Court, Castle Wynd, Inverness, on Monday June 19   at 2.30 p.m. Signed D. Ross.

In Erch's house, Jean wanted to know:

"Whaat's th' meeneen o' thus?"

"Ah dudn't do ut," chimed Erch.

"An dud Andy do ut?"

"Naw," said Erch.

"An' who dud ut then?"

"Ah donno."

However much she tried she could get no more out of Erch.

The same scene was enacted next door, and reported to the fathers when they came home.

Both boys were really in the dog house and the tears flowed.

The two fathers got together. They were both rather

perplexed. While they doubted whether the boys were telling the truth, they both had an uneasy feeling that perhaps they were. They agreed to club together and go to Robert Robb the Lawyer, even if he was called Robber Robb. The Old Man had been a witness some time before for a contractor client of Robb's who was suing for an unpaid account. Robb had been pleased with the Old Man's evidence, and told him that was what won the case. Robb remembered the Old Man, and said that although he did not usually take police court cases, he would make an exception. He asked to see the boys.

The boys were scrubbed, dressed in Sunday clothes, and wheeled over the river to Robb's office, up a stair in Cuthbert's Close, where a gas light burned permanently. Everywhere in Robb's room were masses of papers and books, dust covered. Even the floor did not escape. There was a small avenue of unpolished lino from the door to his desk, papers on either hand. The fireplace was full of coal ash, and a clock in a marble stand stood stopped on the mantel-piece. The scene was both depressing and over-powering. The four, boys and parents, were made to sit by the desk on rather rickety kitchen chairs. He was a rough one, was Robb. He grilled the boys unmercifully until the tears flowed.

The most he could get was:

"Ah dudn't do ut an' ah donno who dud."

After the grilling Robb was quite pleasant. "I think I know the position," he said. "I'll see you in court, and remember, boys, in court I only want the truth. I'll tell you when to come."

At the appointed time Robb appeared in court and tendered a plea of "Not Guilty," for both boys, and had the trial fixed for 28th June, on which day the two boys and two fathers were in attendance at the Castle Wynd. The police office and court room were opposite the fire station. The boys were in a state of too great terror to admire the gleaming fire engine.

The drunks and petty thieves of the weekend fell to be dealt with first. They came from the holding cells at the back

130

of the office, each cell furnished with a hair mattress on the flagstone floor, and a toilet with no cover or chain release.

The desk sergeant kept them in his office, and while they waited, there were those who had been dealt with in Heaven above, and were returned to the cells for onward routing to Porterfield Prison. There were those who were fined and paid or had time to pay, and were having their personal belongings, of which they were relieved on arrest, returned to them.

There was a hustle and a bustle up and down the stone stairs which led to the court, and a general air of excitement in which the boys, with hollow stomachs, could take no pleasure.

Eventually a policeman came clattering down the stairs shouting "MacDougall and Macrae!" The quartet ascended to the place of judgment.

They entered the court at well level. To their right was the dock, and behind, a steep tier of six or eight stepped benches for the public. Baillie MacGillivray sat high to their left, and below him, facing the court, the town clerk, as clerk of court. On his right was the witness stand, and on his left the press seats. Between the town clerk and the dock was a long table, the bar, for the solicitors. There Robbie sat alone. To Robbie's right sat the prosecutor, Chief Constable MacNaughton. The court looked crummy, neglected, uncharitable, cold comfort for any alleged transgressor of the law of the land.

There was a look of supreme boredom on the face of the prosecutor, as he shovelled impatiently at his papers. The story was told of him that on an occasion when a young solicitor brought an armful of books for a trial, he blurted out:

"We don't want any of your dam' law here."

Baillie MacGillivray had arthritis. In his very best of moods he was very testy. The Old Man's face fell when he saw him on the bench.

The Baillie rapped on his desk and called "Ordurr." A silence fell. The clerk in a well modulated voice called for Andrew MacDougall and Archibald Macrae. A policeman, acting as court officer beckoned, and as the two fathers stood up, they were placed with their offspring in front of the dock.

The court officer called:

"All witnesses in this case leave the court."

Mr and Mrs Aitken left with Davie Ross.

The prosecutor rose and said "This is a window breaking case, y'r Honour. Ther's too much of thus goeen on, an' that's why I brott thus case."

"Wet a meenut," said the Baillie, "let the clerk read the complaint."

The clerk read out the contents of the bit of blue paper delivered at the homes.

The prosecutor said "Ma furst wutness is Missus Aitken," who was produced and placed in the witness stand.

"Holld y'r right haand up an' say efter me," and Mrs Aitken took the oath.

The prosecutor's questions established the day and time of the incident, that the boys were playing football in the street, and that the ball struck and broke the window. The boys were formally identified. The prosecutor sat down satisfied, and Robb got up.

"Do you see in court the person who broke your window?"

"No," said Mrs. Aitken.

"Do you know who broke your window?"

"Neil Mackay. Ah saa hum throo the wundow kick the baal."

Robb looked at the prosecutor and said "You may want to do something about that."

The prosecutor, angry, with the frustration all too evident in his voice said "Ah dusert thus ces, Y'r Honour."

The Baillie, no less displeased that his time should have been so wasted, said "Ces dusmussed," stood up, and without the shadow of a bow, stamped from the court.

The two fathers paused only for a brief thankyou to Robb, tripped down the stairs, sent the boys home, and made straight for Gellion's suitably to celebrate.

The boys were in great glee. They were heroes in the

school. They had been to court and got off. They were required to tell the story time and time again, and each time it acquired more frills. Gone were the hollow stomachs. Many were the brief privileges, such as an unusually large share of their mates' sweets, the dowt (core) of an apple, help with the homework, and a whisper of an answer to a classroom question. Did the teacher concede a little admiration too?

The Courier reported the case without names the following day. The leader had a short reference to the incompetence of the police, who brought stupid charges without full investigation, wasteful of the time of the court and all concerned.

In due course the Old Man went to see Robb again by appointment.

"What is it this time?" said Robb.

"Ah waant t' pey y'r account."

"Do you know Richard Balfour?" said Robb. Balfour was a well-known and wealthy philanthropist and eccentric.

"Ah know hum by sight, but not to speak to," said the Old Man. Few got near enough to Balfour to speak to him in any case.

"Well," said Robb, "as soon as he got his *Courier*, Balfour came here and paid my account."

Two days later Erch was treating himself to a free scud hanging onto the back of Brooke's lorry. Davie Ross hauled him off, and gave him a dallacher round the lug.

Neil Nags was never prosecuted, and tried to get himself in on the act, but clearly, according to the code, his was the role of villain.

133

Harmony And Dis –

ONLY TWO professionals visited Erch's house socially, attracted by Jean's baking and superb teas.

One was a banker, at any rate he classified himself as a banker because he clerked in a bank, and he was very genteel. But there was no question of Mr Walton's ability to play the piano, and no persuasion was required to induce him to perform. Trouble was he never played a tune anyone knew, and the alternating reflex rise of right hand, left hand into the air gave much mirth to the boys. Safely under the table, hidden by an ample cover, they imitated the great man, choking with glee till Andy grew too enthusiastic. He knocked his knuckles on the underside of the table top letting out a squeak of pain, which moved Jean to banish both to the kitchen.

Erch thought Miss Fraser and Mr William Kemp who battered away before the silent screen in the La Scala were streets ahead. Their music was required to bear some relation to the action on the screen. A love scene was accompanied by romantic music. The sheriff and his posse chasing the rustlers at full gallop, hotted up the tempo to the beat of the charging horses' hooves. All great musical improvisation, and most of it by ear.

Probably it was only because he was a captive for tea that Walton condescended to address an urchin. He had once met Lord Rothermere, an event never to be forgotten. It is doubtful if any words were exchanged, but even lords require to visit Banks at times.

Walton was also in the world of voice culture, for was not his favourite niece a leading member of the choral society conducted by Lewis J. Owen, and also of the light opera company, not to mention the church choir? She had sung with the great choir of seven hundred voices in the Northern Meeting Park in 1920. That was the first public appearance of the Inverness Silver Band, subsidised by the town council to the extent of ½d on the rates. Unhappily there were difficulties in retaining a bandmaster tutor, and in the absence of a local brass tradition, the band finally broke up in 1936, when the instruments were lent to the Inverness District Asylum.

"End," said Walton, addressing Erch grudgingly, "would you laike to play in instrument?"

"Ah w'd like to play th' pipes."

The wrong thing to say. To Walton the pipes were not music but a horror.

Not all shared his view, for Erch and Andy and hundreds of townspeople followed the British Legion Band religiously, marching behind them proudly to the Islands where they performed on summer evenings. Of all their followers, the Legion gave preferential treatment to a well-known local worthy, Alex Duff. Alex, the friend of all, was permitted to walk alongside the pipe major, which he did with great dignity.

To a marked degree the legion band was fed by the Boys Brigade Band, so efficiently tutored and managed by their dedicated pipe major John Hunter. This able young band played on all Brigade occasions, besides assisting often in local charitable causes.

Walton tried again. "Do you ever listen to Mr. Meny's orchestra in the Islands?"

Known as Herr Meny's Harmony, the Islands Orchestra of piano and ten strings, was supported by local subscription. They played throughout three weeks of the summer from 1927 till 1932, romantic and light classical music. Some thought the locus unsuitable because of the sound of the waterflow, and sometimes the noise of playful children. But the glorious sylvan setting surely compensated for any such drawbacks.

"Oh aye, ah like Herr Meny. Never thought a German cood be so nice. Carry his museek or his vilin f'r hum

135

summtimes. Speeks Engleesh funny.''

"So you would laike to pley the violin?''

"Och no, th' pipes. Butt ah like the vilin. Ah ofen lissen t' th' Strathspey an' Reel un th' Glenalbyn Hotel practiseen. When they oppen aal th' wundows y' c'n heer them fine un Young Street. And,'' volunteered Erch for good measure, "ah know th' maan thaat waves th' white stuck aat them.''

He felt no call to mention he had been chased by the conductor Alex Grant for pinching his turnips at Tomnahurich Farm.

"Well done little men. You may yet become a membah of our illustrious musical fraternity.''

At this stage Walton felt he had fulfilled his duty. He found it oppressive conversing with such a common child. He sat back, permitting his thoughts to assume their more accustomed elevated plane.

Walton did not know of the Old Man's friendship with Jeremy Rudford, the English fellow who worked in the Rose Street Foundry as a fitter, and who played the flute in the Salvation Army Band. Jeremy was highly skilled. He made his own flute from steel, and it sounded every bit as good as the wooden version. He also turned out tin whistles while you cough. With Jeremy he sometimes went to Miss Sarah Walker's subscription concerts in the Music Hall – when the fare was not too heavy.

Andy's father was a bit of a singer too. He had a powerful baritone and a good repertoire of Scots songs, many of which Andy could reproduce in a fair to middling voice.

But the great love of both boys was reserved for the pipes, and wherever the pipes played, there they would be. Their interest reached its climax on the day the Northern Meeting first fielded a combined band of one hundred pipers.

"Maan ut waas Graan.''

Succour In Affliction

"WHY ARE y' baakeen t'day?" asked Erch. It was a Wednesday. Baking was for Friday.

"Dr Morag's cummeen," said Jean.

The second professional who visited Erch's was Dr Morag, small, rotund, red cheeked, bespectacled – horn rims, which were not so commonplace then. A rich crop of black hair was piled up on top of her head, secured by hairpins, which were liable to pop out at the most inconvenient moments – could be into the tea cup or the soup plate. Dr Morag had the most jovial of personalities and an infectious laugh. She covered her practice on a bicycle but became one of the earliest on four wheels. Her first car was like a horse cab converted to power, and had two great polished brass paraffin lamps up front to show the way by night. She did not drive herself, and the cost of a chauffeur must have made a vast inroad upon her income.

Andy and Erch delighted in making comic faces into the lamps and getting grotesque responses from the mirrors.

Dr Morag too was attracted by Jean's baking, and, no mean eater, she gloried in the scones brought straight from the oven to the table, where they were liberally smothered in fresh butter and raspberry jam. It was a joyous revelation to see a body enjoy her food as did Dr Morag.

Unlike the well-bred ducal Walton, Dr Morag was every boy's auntie, and chatted up Andy and Erch as though she was family.

Jean had recalled for Erch how marvellous she had been when epidemics struck. In the scarlet fever crisis in 1928 when there were 78 cases, she was in the thick of the fray, and was instrumental in having the children's ward in the

137

Infirmary closed. As though that were not enough there were 150 cases of diptheria the same year, and she was a leader in the drive for immunisation. That year Culduthel Hospital, then concentrating on tuberculosis, (20 deaths per annum) could not cope, and the Citadel (originally for smallpox and cholera) was opened up. Primitive as it was, it was finally abandoned as unsuitable in 1929.

In 1923 she was in the midst of a massive chickenpox outbreak. The same year this disease became notifiable, because of the similarity of symptoms to smallpox.

How relieved this caring doctor was when the tuberculosis pavilion for 24 cases was opened at Culduthel in 1923, and had electricity and central heating installed a year or two later.

Erch himself contracted chickenpox, and he scratched for three weeks in bed, despite the nails being cut back to the quick, and the warnings to leave the spots. The body marks of the spots were badges of office for years to come, until gradually they faded.

Mumps were rampant in 1928 and to minimise the spread Dr Morag played her part in having all schools closed for three weeks.

Erch escaped mumps, but Andy, however, was not so fortunate. He was obliged for forget his appetite, and exist on liquids. In a couple of weeks he went thin as a rake, but once returned to a wholesome diet he was quickly restored to full bloom.

But when the ambulance called at Jock the Donal's door, there was no room for hilarity. Here was the killer, scarlet, come right into the school and the classroom. And worse still Jock went to the Citadel because Culduthel was crowded. There was a spontaneous movement among his mates to contribute to the alleviation of his suffering, and if possible, to promote his cure.

Many paid a penny a week. The teacher got wind of the movement and suggested the money be given to Jock's mother to buy whatever she thought suitable. So half a crown went to Jock's mother for three weeks. Jock was a popular boy. When he did return to school he was a shadow of his former self, but he soon made up the leeway, and was on the shinty field again where he excelled, which was more than could be said for his performance in the classroom.

Like most of her profession, Dr Morag was in 1925 a leader in the drive to raise £100,000 for an extension to the Northern Infirmary. There was a massive movement throughout the whole north. She had the satisfaction of seeing the Mackintosh of Mackintosh cut the first sod in November 1927, Mr Walter Elliott, Secretary of State lay the foundation stone in May 1928, and the Duke of York (later King George VI) open the completed building in May 1929. Authority to use the "Royal" prefix was conferred in September 1929.

Erch and Andy visited the Infirmary carrying a few grapes for Angie Urk, who, like many others, was sent for the extraction of tonsils, a minor operation very respectable at the time. For adults, appendicitis was the vogue. These apart, this hospital dealt with masses of more serious cases, and a multitude had cause to be grateful for its ministrations – substantially conferred free by general practitioners.

When up at the Leachkin to play shinty or football, very often a party from the Asylum (now Craig Dunain) was encountered making for or coming from the quarry where they broke stones by hand for road metal. They looked so strange, it was eerie. The name "Asylum" was dreaded. Abandon all hope all ye who enter here. Visions of locked doors and despair. Andy and Erch always felt rather sadly uncomfortable meeting these parties, knowing nothing of the devoted work carried on in the Asylum. Clearly it was a huge organisation with seven to eight hundred patients, and developments between the wars to the extent of the provision of a hall, a nurses' home, electricity supply, and central heating. Perhaps fortunately, the Asylum did not impinge much on the consciousness of school children, for by far the greater number of patients came from outside Inverness.

Muirfield was different.

"Waant y' t' tek scones up t' old Hector," said Andy's mum.

139

"Whaat, th' Poor House?" asked Andy.

"Ut's no th' Poor House. Ut's Mewerfield Unstutewt."

A visit to Muirfield was not the most popular chore for Andy and Erch, but they knew old Hector, a nice man, who went there on the death of his wife. They were never allowed beyond the reception area, where the institutional smell of the stockpot violently assailed their nostrils, to become in their minds, the badge of this valuable hospice. Sometimes they would see an old man in a wheel chair. Infirmity in old age is not a sight readily bearable to the very young.

Unhappily it represented for many the disgrace of the parish, and the very thought of being consigned to its walls gave rise to a feeling of abhorrence. Nevertheless, it was filled with those who had none to turn to, and it had a caring administration.

Their duty at Muirfield completed, Andy and Erch elected to pursue their homeward way by High Street and Academy Street. Reaching the Central Hall Picture House, they turned down School Lane to Church Street.

"Look at thaat," said Andy pointing to a house in Church Street, formerly the Free Church Manse, now Clansman Hotel.

"Whaat?" asked Erch.

"See whaat ut seys."

Erch too looked at the graphics above the ground floor windows, which read IDA MERRY MATERNITY HOME. They knew IDA stood for Inverness District Asylum, because that was the name of the Asylum football team.

"Why," wondered Erch, "Hes th' Asylum gott a Maternity Home an' whaat's merry about utt?"

This was formerly known as the Bowmount Centre. Because of the very active support given by the Hon Mrs Ida Merry, Belladrum, the name was changed in her honour. This centre did grand work in the field of maternity, both for those who could contribute to cost, and for those who could not.

There were sometimes messages to carry to the Isobel Fraser Home of Rest, a haven for old folk who could make

140

some contribution to their keep. These visits did not generate the same distaste as those to Muirfield, because the residents here were required to have a minimum standard of health.

Founded by Mrs Fred Fraser in 1906, it functioned first at 42 Charles Street, moved in 1927 to Viewhill, Culduthel Road, and in 1938 to the present beautiful purpose-built home in Mayfield Road. The name of Mrs E.C. Jack was for 30 years associated with it, and it still provides a wonderful service to the community.

Both boys knew the collector for the Blind Institute, who made an annual call at all houses for contributions, seldom meeting a rebuff. The great work of this Institute has continued since 1861.

"Ther's a little blaak baby unn ther." So said Jean to Erch, pointing to the older part of the present Regional Buildings, originally a college. It was the Northern Counties Infant Home, established in 1916, and moved to Rosedene, Island Bank Road, where its work continues. The name of Mrs Fraser Mackenzie was for many years closely associated.

"Snowball," was the evocative name applied by the Hon Mrs Esme Smyth, Ness Castle, to her annual cash and comforts drive to help the Highland Orphanage, founded in 1880, and having its own school of 80 pupils. The highly original title of the winter time appeal contributed to its success, and in most houses in the street there was a great clearance of used clothes and toys. and a baking and toffee making for the sale.

Present day state provision from the cradle to the grave contrasts sharply with these former days when so many caring organisations required generous support from townspeople. Young people of the time could not but be conscious that the disadvantaged depended so much upon those more favoured by fortune.

The invaluable Institutions devoted to public service, survived only because their demands were nobly met by ordinary citizens.

Mixed Grill

"WHAAT Y' GOTT f'r homewurk?" Andy wanted to know.

"Copyeen. We gott copy books now. Up light, down heavy, an' nevur luft y'r pen tull y' cumm t' th' end o' th' wurd."

"'They cumm as a boon an' a blessing to men, t' Puckwuck, th' owl, an' th' Waverley pen,'" quoted Andy. "Whaat kind o' nub d' you use?"

"Ah use a Waverley."

"Me too. Nice an' thun an' ut opens out when y' press down."

"Any books?" asked Erch.

"Aye, hev waan or two. Ah'll go an' gett them."

Both boys retreated homewards, returning shortly with their offerings to swap.

Erch offered the *Wizard* and the *Adventure* for Andy's *Dixon Hawke*. Wizard and Adventure were the next stage up from comics – *Tiger Tim's* and *Rainbow*. They had very few cartoons and provided good reading, some short stories, some serials. Heroes were strong men or clever detectives, or maybe they had supernatural powers. They always were GOOD men. About the same weight as *Wizard* and *Adventure* were the schoolboy stories of the *Gem* with its hero Tom Merry, and the *Magnet*, featuring Harry Wharton. There was little to choose between these two. Tom Merry probably had the edge, his name sounding more acceptable. Dixon Hawke and Sexton Blake represented the very early, if not the first paperback form. About five inches square, they were staple bound and had about 100 pages. They were the great detectives of the time, and theirs was the world of the Whodunnit, a word awaiting invention.

The two made the exchange, and were equipped for a read on a winter Sunday.

"Ian's gott a gramophone," said Andy. "Gott flat records like plates, not tubes like your phonograph."

"Phonograph's old fashioned. Can't buy records now. An' th' ones we gott 'r no much good."

"The saams 'r no good, but Laader's no baad wi' 'We pairted on th' shore.' Wouldn't mind heering that agen."

"C'm on then an' ah'll see eff ah'll gett t' pley ut."

Jean allowed the use of the phonograph – it was old-fashioned anyway, and it wouldn't matter much if they broke it. Erch put the instrument on top of the washtub cover, and carefully extracted a cylindrical box from the big tin which held nine of them. The box was very stoutly made with a tight fitting lid and a woolly felt lining inside which the record lay. He inserted his fingers into the black cylinder which was the record as he was taught to do, and extracted "We pairted on the shore," placing it on the metal cylinder which lay horizontally on top of the machine. He stuck a big horn into the sound box, inserted the winder in the side of the machine and wound up. He switched on and a garbled lot of squeaks came out. What was wrong? The record had been placed back to front. The necessary correction was made, and this time Lauder took it away in a squeaky, scratchy, nasal voice. It wasn't bad, but it wasn't good either. The machine was returned to its corner in the parlour.

"Gemm o' snakes 'n ladders?"

Andy agreed, and they had a go at that, at Ludo, dominoes, and put and take with spent matches for stakes. Then they heard the High Kirk bell – eight o'clock, and the end of the day – at least so it was in winter. In summer the elders were sometimes prevailed upon, especially during the holidays, to give licence until the ten o'clock bell. But that was final.

On bells, there was another on the first Thursday of each month, to call in the councillors for their monthly meeting. Nothing to do with our boys, but it was fun for them sometimes to see how many they could identify stepping up to the town hall.

While the town slept, the young bloods could be engaged

143

in another activity – dancing. The dance started at 8 p.m. and ended at 4 a.m. The rendezvous were the Rose Street Drill Hall, the Lovat Scout Hall, for slightly more posh the Queensgate Hotel, and, really top drawer, the Northern Meeting Rooms. Dan Mackintosh, Don Taylor, and Ken Sim were among the best known band leaders, and could depend upon one, if not two, engagements per week. They were not full timers, but they deployed a piano, saxophone, violin and drums, with sometimes a banjo. These functions were unlicensed, but a cup of tea and buns were provided at midnight. In the main they were promoted by charitable organisations for fund raising purposes. The major hotels had not yet realised the profit potential of integral ballrooms, and in any case there was so much opposition to late licences, it wasn't worth the candle. The most prominent of the licensed dances was known as the Police Ball (Burgh Bobbies) held on the night before the January Fast Day. That was a recognised rave, and a good night for burglary.

Dances apart, the late night hours found the streets of Inverness deserted except for the night duty policemen, conscientiously pounding their beats, and the prowler up to no good.

"Your sister go to dances, Andy?"

"Aye, she goes sumtimes wi' her couseen when hees home fr'm Ewniverseety."

"Wull you go t' dances when y'r big?"

"Naw. Ut's only Jessies thaat go t' dances. Ah'll nevurr go."

"Nor me neether."

There were those, exponents of the Charleston and the Syncopated Dip, only eight years their seniors, who would bet on a change of faith. They were the backbone of the St Louis Palais de Danse in the Queensgate Hotel.

"Whaat d' y' think y'll be when y'r big, Andy?"

"Think ah'll be a jiner. Ma Granfather's a jiner. Good job. Whaat about you?"

"Ah always waanted t' be a mulkman. Ah'm no shoor

144

now. Ah'd rather be an enjin driver, or a sailor an' see a butt o' th' wurld."

They had plenty of time to think.

Jeemie Ayburdeen

THE FIRST of his age group in the street to provide himself with a bike was Jock. He made it himself – well, he may have had some help from Andrew the Smith, for it was in Andrew's smiddy it was built. The bits had been collected from a scrapyard and garden sheds around the area, and stuck together to make quite a workable bike. That there were no brakes did not worry Jock. A foot on the front tyre did just as good, and there were no mudguards to get in the way.

It was autumn and the nights were drawing in. On a Friday evening Jock announced in the street that the following day he was going with his older cousin Arty for a run by bike to Dores. Erch's eyes gleamed. At home at tea time he consulted the Old Man about the road to Dores. The Old Man volunteered that in his young days there was a right of way by the river and Loch Dochfour to Bona and Dores, but the only bit that remained was at Ness Castle, where there was a small well made road for the fishers, and a footpath continuing through Laggan, Borlum and Ballindalloch to Bona. And how far was Ness Castle? Well, to the Swiss Cottage about four miles, and to Bona Ferry another three.

Erch went to consult with Andy.

"Whaat about askeen Jock and his cousin f'r a lift t' Ness Castle. We cood tek a piece an' waak t' Bona, cross th' ferry, an' baak th' other side. W'll y' get a penny f'r th' ferry?"

"Oh aye," said Andy.

Jock was approached, and he was delighted to accommodate.

The four set out at nine the following morning by the Suspension Bridge, Ness bank, Island Bank and Dores

Roads. Andy and Erch had to perch seatless on the cross bars of the bikes, hanging on to the handlebars. They were uncomfortable seats, but what matter discomfort for the sake of an exciting adventure into the unknown? They hadn't to walk until they came to the humped back bridge at Ness Side, and then again on Ness Castle Brae. Jock and Arty pedalled hard, a bit bandy legged because of their passengers, but they made light of their task.

On the stretch between Ness Side and Swiss Cottage there was a stone wall on their left, the boundary at that point of Ness Castle Estate. Arty stopped the party to view a big, flat stone in the wall with the word STAR printed in roadside tar. Arty was knowledgable. He had been that way before.

At the turn of the century, a party of young cavalry officers, billeted in Aldourie Castle, had had an evening of drinking in the Highland Club. At 11.30 p.m. one of the officers, moved to bravado by the demon, said, "I'll be in Aldourie Castle by midnight, or in hell."

He set out at full gallop along Wade's road to Dores, but his horse stumbled in the dark, and he was thrown into the ditch, badly injured. In his own blood, he printed the name of his horse on the stone − STAR − and both rider and horse had been found dead the following morning. The boys thrilled to the tale.

Half a mile on, Jock said, "Right y'r on y'r own."

Swiss Cottage was a delightful little round house, timber-built on stilts. Somebody must have copied a picture from the Swiss Alps, and very successfully. In its sylvan setting it fitted beautifully into the landscape.

It stood at the junction of two roads forking in roughly the same direction, both leading to the river. The boys chose the one to the right which took them through Ness Castle Farm. Downstream they could see the lower weir, but their route was upstream. A boat with one rod and a ghillie was plying a fly above the upper weir − otherwise no life. The two roads met by the upper weir and became one, right up to the Laggan boundary of Capt Kemble. On the Laggan beat John Reidpath was fishing single-handed. He was a man of infinite patience and superb skill, who thought nothing of fishing the whole night through. Who had said of him, "He could take a fish out of a piece of wet cement"?

The going was easy, and it was interesting. Soon they were opposite Dochfour water, and they could see the banks of the canal rising on the other side, near Dochgarroch.

They were carefully negotiating a wet patch when two cracks from a gun scared them out of their wits. A man rose from the riverside, a gun under his arm. In his concentration he had not seen the boys.

"Mussed th' buggar," he said.

"Whaat'r y' shooting at?" asked Erch.

"Ah'm efter mergansers. They play th' very devul wi' th' samun. Ah've had three this week already. Wher y' goeen?"

"Bona."

"Och well, y' won't be long. Y'll hutt a goodish rodd un a wee while at Ballindalloch."

That they soon found true, for when the river opened out to Loch Dochfour, they came on a narrow road fit for vehicles, and so they reached Bona, very pleased with themselves.

The ferry was less than a hundred yards across, and the ferryman, Willie Macdonald, a canal employee, lived in the lighthouse on the other side. Willie had to be summoned by hoisting a board three feet square to the top of a high post by the jetty.

They hoisted the board and looked anxiously across to see if it was to be answered. No life could be seen at the lighthouse, and as the stomachs proclaimed it was time to eat, they sat on a tree trunk by the jetty and ate their pieces, washing them down with loch water scooped up in cupped hands.

They took an interest in Mr Luke's geese in the field nearby, and in a well dressed lady, mounted on a tall sleek brown horse, and proceeding sedately the way they had come. How easily she sat, and how contented looked the mount.

148

Through the narrows they could see Loch Ness, with a slight easterly ruffling its otherwise still surface.

It was not cold, but they were not enjoying hanging around knowing they still had a journey to make.

At last a stocky man came out of the lighthouse building opposite, stepped into a rowboat, and with his back to them and an oar over the stern, sculled the boat in a dead straight line across the ferry to the point at which they were waiting. The boys approached the boat, but Willie Macdonald, for it was indeed he, called, "Pit doon th' bord furst." Andy lowered the board and the two clambered into the boat.

"Sutt wher y' like," said Willie, pushing the boat off with his oar, and sculling back whence he came, again in a dead straight line, causing the boys to exchange glances of silent admiration.

There wasn't much point in asking him questions, for his back was to them.

Once ashore, the boys proffered a penny each, which Willie took absently. He observed the jersevs, the shorts, the boots, and the haircuts, and made up his mind.

"You fr'm Unvurnes?"

"Aye," said Andy.

"Whaat's y'r nems?" The names were given.

"Wer d'y luv?" The addresses were given.

"Ah thunk ah know y'r Dad," he said to Erch.

"Aye, he said he knew you."

"Used t' meet hum when ah wurked 'n th' Gondolier. Went t' Temple Pier a lot."

The boys were warming to this old man and they dared to ask him about the sculling and how he kept in a straight line. He was happy to explain it to them. If he kept the lighthouse or the jetty on the other side right in the middle of his stern, he would travel in a straight line from point to point.

"Ut's quite eesy, rite enuff."

Then they asked him about his work at the lighthouse, and all about the boats that passed. Realising that time marched Erch asked, "Hev y' gott th' rite time?" On the question of time, it was always the done thing to ask for the RIGHT time. Any other time would not do. Willie took out a big watch from a waistcoat pocket and announced it was three o'clock, and quietly handed back the pennies which had never been transferred to his pocket.

They felt they had to be on their way, and soon they were on the main road heading back to Inverness. They both agreed it was a bit of a bore walking on the main road. Andy's father belonged to the Leachkin, and Andy knew that area quite well. He looked to the hillside at the left, and said if they climbed to the top and walked on they would come to the Leachkin. It wouldn't be much longer.

They were lucky to choose as their line of ascent the burn running into Loch Dochfour a little north-east of Dochfour House. Anywhere else they would have encountered precipitous sides and danger. In the Gaelic the burn is called the Cascade of the Battle. In years later they were to read that the burn passed by the site of a battle between, on the one side, Edward I's governor of Urquhart Castle, and, on the other, an ambushing force of the Earl of Moray, who, with Wallace, was seeking to rid Scotland of the English. Moray prevailed, but the govenor escaped back to Urquhart.

The trackless climb was becoming stiffer and steeper, calling for many rests to get the breath back, and many sips from the Cascade to keep cool. They reached and crossed the Blackfold Road, and at last they seemed to be on top. They looked down upon the Glen and across to Strathnairn. They also saw below something they had missed on the climb — a herd of about twenty wild goats.

In a dip near the head of the burn they stumbled upon a spherical rusty iron pot about two feet six inches in diameter, with a pipe coming out of the top, curling round and round like a corkscrew. Erch wondered what might be cooked in that kind of pot, and what was it doing in such a remote place. Erch decided to ask the Old Man. He knew all right — wasn't he a cork medallist in the Freemasons?

They turned their heads north-east to follow the line of the ridge. The going was very heavy, tough heather up to their waists, and a rough and sometimes boggy surface. It was slow going because each step had to be taken gingerly. Then almost without warning, they found themselves enveloped in wet fog blown in from the firth, bringing visibility down to ten feet. Soon, as often happens in the eerie thickness of fog, they completely lost their sense of direction. They stopped to discuss their predicament, and agreed the falling slope should be kept to their right. With this in mind they plodded on, making sure not to lose height, until at last they came to a fence running at right angles to their course. Hardly had they touched it than there rose almost at their feet a fawn apparition which loped easily away from them, sure footed, making a scything sound as it passed through the heather. A roe deer.

They both agreed if they turned left and followed the fence they should sometime come to the track which led to the Leachkin. This they did, staggering on, now soaked by the wet heather and the moisture laden fog. After what seemed an eternity they reached another fence at right angles, and on the other side could see a well-beaten track. They climbed the fence, and turned right on the track. It was a merciful release to be able to walk heather free, without having to worry about foot holds.

In the thickness of the fog they had no idea whether it was still daylight or dark. The sounds of their boots as they met stones on the track, seemed to echo around them. They were becoming very unhappy with exhaustion and hunger.

After an age, a bright glow penetrated the gloom ahead, and a rough voice grunted aggressively, "Who's thayre?" They could have been afraid, but on the other hand what a relief it was to meet another human being! Erch said "Us," and moved into the circle of the glowing fire. Seated by it, resting on one elbow, was the scruffiest of men, his great tackety boots stretching across the track, socks about his ankles to reveal great hairy legs. The trousers were moleskins, and he wore a heavy nondescript grey coat, a muffler, and a shapeless bonnet. He had a large unshaven jaw, a heavy brown moustache, and uneven blackish teeth – truly an evil looking apparition to meet in the wilds and in the dark. Erch recognised him – Jeemie Ayburdeen – a poacher who had often brought his produce to the Old Man

151

– a couple of rabbits, a brace of pigeons, and sometimes a haunch of venison. He was a man of about sixty. He must have been a benign poacher, or the keepers of Dochfour Estate would have hounded him from their preserves.

"Who's us?"

Jeemie had a good look at the boys and grunted at Erch – "Seen you before." Erch identified himself, and the atmosphere, at first guarded, became quite warm. Erch told the story of their journey so far.

"Hungry?" asked Jeemie. He did not need to ask. The smell of cooking which rose from his fire made the boys feel absolutely ravenous. With hand as black as coal Jeemie handed each a toasted rabbit leg, a bit burnt on the outside, but in their state, ambrosia. They sat down by the fire, and, with the greatest relish, greedily ate the rabbit flesh.

Jeemie had no watch, and didn't know the time, "rite" or otherwise, but he reckoned it would be about ten o'clock. Ten o'clock! Two hours dark and they were expected home in daylight. Their host estimated they were about two miles from home. The boys thought they had better move, and quick. They thanked Jeemie for his hospitality, and set course for home, fast.

Soon they found themselves by the little mission hall at the top of the Leachkin – familiar territory now!

Down the Leachkin brae at a trot, over the canal locks, and down a deserted Fairfield Road. At this level there was no fog, but the dark was little relieved by the gas street lights. The street was deserted until they reached the first houses, when they met a man going in the opposite direction.

When they were within arm's distance he struck a match and held it up to their faces.

"Aye," he said, "it's you."

It was the Old Man.

Bikes

F IRST THERE were scooters, the most popular, and the cheapest, made of wood with wooden wheels. This was a rackety vehicle which gave no sense of speed. Andy's father picked up something much better, made of steel, with solid rubber tyres. This could get up some speed on the cement pavements of Kenneth Street, to the dismay of pedestrians and the elderly.

The action in riding a scooter was the first step to riding a bike. But bikes were expensive – £2 10/- for a Hercules, and £5 for a Raleigh.

Andy's elder sister had a bike, and a lady's bike was the best for practice. Though they couldn't reach the seat Andy and Erch trundled up and down the back yard, first scooter wise, then getting a turn or a half turn of the pedals, in the restricted space. Time came when they had to try the road. Andy found his first go on the road exciting – the speed was great. Away he went to King Street, and round the corner. But tragedy! He was wearing sandshoes. With no heels to latch on to the pedals, both feet slipped, and he found himself up to the armpits in handlebars, and steering an impossibility. He was stopped by a lamp-post, and fortunately unhurt. But the bike was not so lucky, with handlebars 45° out, and the front wheel buckled.

By 1928 the *Courier* was describing Inverness as a town on wheels. Bikes were everywhere. When the Academy and High School pupils were released, a mass of bicycles descended upon the town by Stephen's Brae and Crown Drive, taking possession of the centre, and flashing through the archway of the Suspension Bridge. Added to the congestion were the numerous bikes of message boys from grocers, butchers, ironmongers, fruiterers and others. These had a fixed container for a large, square basket in front, and sometimes at the rear also. There were various congregating places for message boys, the most popular being at the foot of Culduthel Road, where no doubt the boys felt a rest necessary before negotiating the brae to the hill district. The correspondence columns of the *Courier* carried complaints, but to no effect.

There were constant prosecutions – no lights, and after 1928 no reflectors, cycling on pavements, reckless cycling, and leaving cycles outside shops. Cycling on Stephen's Brae was prohibited in 1929, but continued until all were frightened off by prosecutions. Chief Constable MacNaughton said in the police court it was an offence to come down on one pedal, and it was even later established a contravention to walk a bike up or down the brae.

There was an agitation for better roads because of danger to and from cyclists, and for side tracks on roads to segregate cyclists .

K.J. Mackintosh hired bikes out at 2/6d per week, and there were about half a dozen establishments selling and repairing.

Without doubt the bike had come to play a vital part in the life of the community, and it was both utilitarian and recreational.

It was usual for boys to graduate to bikes before leaving the primary school. Up to that time much borrowing was done, and it was common to see boys on bikes much too big – simply straddling the bar without a seat, hobbling on the seat, or with one leg through the bar.

Once the possessor of a bike, the boy found it necessary to use it for every journey in excess of fifty yards.

The bike played a very important part after the swimming baths in Montague Row closed. Swims became practical at Bunchrew, Alturlie, Ness Castle, and Dochgarroch. At Dochgarroch on the north side of the canal and within a mile on the Inverness side of the locks, there is a small loch – probably an excavation for clay to bind the banks when the canal was building. An area of this loch was safe for bathing,

"THROUGH THE BAR"

and being stagnant and shallow, was much warmer than sea, river or canal. In colder weather a bike run might extend as far as Nairn to the sea-water indoor pool there.

Cycling on main roads was reasonably comfortable, even though surfaces were sometimes bad. There were few motor vehicles, unlike the present, when the cyclist takes to the roads at his peril.

In 1925 there was a happening of great moment in Inverness, when the magistrates placed police officers to direct traffic at the Inglis Street/High Street and Bridge Street/Church Street corners. A more leisurely occupation could not be conceived. The signals were slow and deliberate, and in the long gaps between, the constables stood rigid like guardsmen, hoping they were being admired by the populace, which turned out in force to see the strange phenomenon. By September the magistrates authorised the use of white gloves by the point duty men, and they became real toffs. Their greatest bugbear was the cyclist, who could dodge quickly past a duty officer, and leave him frustrated by his inability to pursue or identify. There were numerous prosecutions for failure to obey police signals, but in due time discipline prevailed.

Like most innovations this one came to be accepted as part of the local scene, and the Chief Constable applied to increase his force because of the loss of manpower to point duty.

The bikes are still with us, but substantially reduced in numbers, their hey-day eclipsed by that enemy of mankind, the internal combustion engine.

Gondolier And Glengarry

NOTHING CONTRIBUTES more to the excitement of a community than regular visitation by boats, especially of the passenger carrying variety.

The Kessock ferry boat was always a centre of attraction, and so also was the *Ailsa* from Cromarty when she sailed from the Thornbush to cruise in the Cromarty Firth.

These could hardly match for romance the paddle steamers *Gondolier* and *Glengarry*, owned by MacBraynes, and run from the top locks at the head of Fairfield Road. Advertisements appeared in April for the *Gondolier* running regularly to Fort William, Oban, and Glasgow, and for the *Glengarry* cruising to Fort Augustus. The advertisements always mentioned as an aside "Refreshments," and nobody, at least no menfolk, imagined that meant tea. For many the "engine room" was a happy resort, even though the scenery was not matched by that on deck.

The evening of the arrival of the *Gondolier* from Glasgow was the highlight. It was met by several two-in-hand waggonettes, drivers in bowlers, with uniformed hotel porters in attendance to meet guests who had reserved accommodation, and to induce those who had not. The Station Hotel, Royal, Caledonian, and Palace were among those represented, some boasting their own conveyances, and some hiring from MacRae and Dick's or Falconer's. Later in time came the charabancs, with canvas hoods lowered when the weather was fair. This spectacle drew an interested crowd on every occasion, attending but to view the intrepid and fortunate travellers, who could afford the luxury of travel by paddle steamer, and to view the smart city clothes they wore.

THE "GONDOLIER"

The steamers provided no overnight accommodation, but that did not detract one bit from the glamour.

There was great bustle as the passengers disembarked, and a great fussing of hotel porters as luggage was claimed, to be parked in the appropriate hotel vehicle. Gradually order came out of chaos, and away went the travellers to dinner in their respective town hotels.

As the spectators dispersed, the crew commenced unloading such cargo as was being carried – nothing dirty enough to sully the gentility of the passengers.

Then came the moment for which Andy, Erch and their like awaited. The ship had to turn round to be ready for the outward journey next day. To do that she had to reverse to a broad part of the canal at Burnfoot, and reverse back. Local urchins were permitted this free scud, and were always there to take advantage – but no gallivanting – there must be discipline on board ship. The Skipper, nearly always a ''Mac'' from the Western Isles more at home in Gaelic than English, liked affording the boys their privilege but brooked no misbehaviour.

What could be more exciting than to watch through the engine room hatch the gleaming pistons working up and down, see the waist-bare stokers shovelling the coal, hear the hiss of escaping steam and the bells of the engine room telegraph, and enjoy the varied smells of – a ship. This was another life and a very attractive one, perhaps even better than being a milkman.

There was a time when these vessels, together with their smaller sister the *Lochness*, served the communities on Loch Ness-side, and called regularly with stores and stock at Adourie, Dores, Abriachan, Temple, Inverfarigaig, Foyers, Glenmoriston and Fort Augustus. Their working life represented a short interlude in the times of the Glen, and a happy one. Now they and their like are gone, also victims of the petrol engine.

At least there are photographs which we can see, and better still there are scale models. The late Mr Donald Mackenzie, while employed as ship's carpenter (chippie) by MacBraynes, made scale models down to the smallest detail

159

of the *Gondolier* and *Glengarry*, each of which demonstrates the great affection he had for them. These are preserved in Inverness Museum.

Others perhaps less glamorous have followed *Gondolier* and *Glengarry*, as they in their turn followed St. Columba's coracles, Cromwell's frigate, and Wade's Highland Galley.

Satisflections

SATURDAY AFTERNOON at the Thatchers. Andy and Erch wandered round to see what was doing. Sandy was there, with John the Plub, Eck the Roads, and Willie the Drains. Eck was a foreman for the town and worked a gang on road repairs. A powerful man, tall and deep voiced and with a black moustache. Willie the Drains was a wee, bandy-legged body, a bit round shouldered, without a spark of humour. His job was to lift the manholes on the roadways, and with a sort of scoop on a long pole, he ladled out the muck into a zinc lined hurley. That wasn't very funny, living daily in the stench of sewage – little wonder he had no sense of humour and some very black nails. They were all puffing pipes, and they were there till the Ordnance opened at five.

When Andy and Erch arrived the topic was the Music Hall.

"Y' know," said Sandy, "We're getteen faar be'er stuff sunce th' Methudists took ovur th' haal than we evur dudd before."

"Thaat's rite," said John, "And th' uthur kurks are complaineen. Say they shoodn't hev concurts un a kurk."

"Ah don't see any herm," said Eck, and that was the general opinion, despite a universal Calvinistic upbringing.

"They'll no hold wi' th' drink tho'," said Willie sadly. That too was agreed, and gave true cause to mourn.

"Funniest thing ah seen ther," said Sandy, "an ut wis free – wis Jamie Mellis' meeteen when he wis stanning f'r th' cooncil. Maan ut wis graan. He hed a big baand playeen thus modrun jazz stuff. Th' hall wis packed, aal cheereen like maad. He wis asked aboot the Loch Ashie vussut – we

161

aal know that's a ploy. They hed mor whusky than they cood drunk – Dunrupple ut waas. They wis aal spuffed sept wan teetotallur, aye th' wholl cooncul but f'r wan rabbut.''

''Mussed thaat,'' said Willie, ''but ah went t' see Dan Dallas un th' Mock Tryul caaled th' Waandurur Maan – ut waas a graan laff. Donal wull be good when he getts a but oldur, an getts some expeerience.''

''Oh aye, that waasn't baad,'' said Eck, ''butt th' waan ah liked waas th' Barnado Boys wi' ther bells. When they played th' tunes wi' aal them bells on th' taable, ah nevur herd anyteen t' touch ut.''

''You go f'r th' museek, Eck,'' said John. ''Me too. Ah went t' heer th' BBC concurt. Thaat waas th' furst time a brodcast wis med fr'm Unvernes. Th' museek waas a butt high faluteen, butt maan thaat wis hustoreek. Stull, f'r museek, give me Scott Skinner. He waas a meen old buggar, butt Goad, he med hus fuddle speek.''

''Y' know ah wis wurkeen on Tomnahureech Street th' uthur day,'' said Eck, ''when a boyan cem askeen me whaat ah rememburred about Unvernes. He waantit t' rite aboot ut un th' Chroneecle. Ah tolld hum no t' be bothereen me jist then. Ah wood thunk aboot ut.''

''Y' cood tell hum aboot th' chucken at Unshes,'' said Willie. ''Ah saaw ut, butt ut waas dedd by then. Ut hed fower legs an fower wungs. Shoor as deth, ah saaw ut. Belonged t' Stewartie th' Chaffoor. Neil Mackintosh sed he w'd gett summ toff un Embraa t' putt ut untull a big jaar, an' puckle ut.''

''Herd aboot thaat,'' said John. ''Nevurr seen ut. Butt ah seen th' blaakburd that nested un Andrew th' Smuth's smiddy. Utt waasn't thaat much fr'm th' aanvul,'' and he stretched out his arms to demonstrate. ''Utt waas rite unn th' muddle of aal thaat hammurring an' shouting, aye an' summtimes curseen. Utt hed three Kyolls, an' they aal gott away safe. Andrew aalways left th' baak door open f'r them t' gett unn an' out.''

''Ah cood tell hum,'' said Eck, ''aboot the seal caat un th' nets aat th' Shott. Med a butt o' a mess o' th' net, butt ah canna say ah liked t' see utt clouted on th' hed. Ah seen utt lookeen up wi' wee eyes, fritened, ut waas, jist like a wee bairn.''

"Th' seal pits me un mind o' th' whale," said Sandy. "Member utt cem ashore at Screetun. Five yerds long ut waas – a spanged ut – five good stepps, an' aboot three spangs fatt. Smuth th' Steevdore gott a squaad t' luft ut on t' a larry wi aboot haff a dozen blocks an' taakle. A lott o' boys wer around an' they helped wi' slings. Smuth sed ut waas at leest two tunns. Went t' Lunndin – th' Bruttish Museem.''

"Whaat aboot aal th' ded boddies they found un coffeens," said Willie. "Ah often found them diggeen f'r drains. Happened at th' Suttadull, an' Culduthull Rodd, an' at Kurkhull an' Balnacregg. They sed summ o' them wis ovurr three thousand yeers olld. Eff we wir luvveen then we wood be dressed un skuns or sumtheen.''

"Cood we nott tell hum aboot some o' th' big shotts we saaw, like King George an' Queen Maary, an' th' Duke o' York, an' th' Prunce o' Waales?" suggested John.

"Aye," said Eck, "an' ther waas Lloyd George, an' Wunstun Churchull, an' Attlee, an' Baldwun. They wer aal rite, butt ah dudn't fancy Harry Laadur, nor Bernard Shaaw. They wer meen, rite enuff. When Barrie cem heer nobody evur saaw hum. They sed he hed a house Drumna-drocheet way.''

"Ther waas anuthur writer maannie," thought Willie. "Funny nemme he hed. Hilleare Belloc. Ah mind becos ma bruthur waas doeen th' bullposteen at th' time, an' he put th' butts th' wrong wey, an' ut cem out Hillebell Aireoc. Gott an' afful telleen off. An' ther waas yon Engleesh chap Wullie Joyce* who blethered un th' town hall aboot th' Faseests.''

"Och y' cood go on an' on," said John looking at his watch. "Five t' five, – c'm on an' see Allunn.''

"Allunn" kept the Ordnance. Off they all went, leaving Andy and Erch just a little wiser.

*Later Lord Haw Haw.

And So . . .

ERCH AND ANDY existed not only in the 20's and 30's.
I am convinced they had their counterparts in every
decade, from the days of the stone cists, to the days of
telstar. True, their counterparts tempered their activity to
their age, and still do, but the instincts were and are the
same.

How well accustomed Erch and his chums were to hearing
from their elders, ''Boys are not what they used to be. God
help the country if we have another war.''

We did, and who criticised the generation sent by the
politicians to fight it?

What youngster dares to say in Inverness, teeming with
places and opportunities for the ploys of boys, ''I've got
nothing to do.''

I believe there always were urchins, and there always will
be. We require to know what they were up to. If we don't,
we haven't got a grasp of social history – the stuff that's
seldom written about, but the stuff that really matters.

I have touched upon the times of one brood, and hope the
times of others will be recorded too.

Taboos

Refusing a fair fight.
Refusing a return fair fight.
Refusing to stop the fight after blood.
Clyping.
Girls.
Bullying.
Weeping after the strap.
Music or dancing lessons.
Cheating.
Wearing a cap.
Wearing long trousers.
Being a mammie's boy.
Throwing stones at birds, cats or dogs.
Scratching the Teacher's back.
Believing in Santa Claus.
Gatecrashing a game of football.
Swotting.
Mugging (boasting or showing off).
Fearing the dark, a dog, a cattle beast, a drunk man or a tinker.

The Games

DURBS OR MARBLES

ORDINARY DURBS could be purchased in most sweetie shops, but the exotics could only be found in Toy Walker's or MacPherson's Sporting Stores. Exotics were seldom purchased, though they were won.

The lowest category of durb was the peejee, little over ½ inch in diameter, and usually of brown clay. The clayack was also of brown clay and about one inch in diameter. The roocher was of white clay, well fired and polished, and this was the one most often used. A deadly antagonist was the steelack, a steel ballbearing obtainable if your father worked in the railway. Glassacks, made of glass and with an internal design, were good players but expensive, and could get chipped. There were a few glassacks, survivors from lemonade bottles. The bottle was secured by a glass sphere in a rubber washer. The last and biggest was the pront, over one inch and a quarter in diameter.

The generation before flicked their durbs in play. The durb was balanced in the bent forefinger, and flicked with the thumb. This generation, degenerate perhaps, threw their durbs.

Follow Me Dedd (dead), two to play
There was a call of ''Back's no follow,'' which gives advantage to the caller A. B has first throw. A throws his durb over three feet ahead in the gutter. B throws to hit it. If successful B throws his durb on. If not and his durb finishes within three feet of A's, B can throw on further. Then it is A's throw. A at any stage in the play (within reason) can claim

CATTIES, GIRDS
& SKIPPING ROPES

"Back's no follow," and can obtain two successive throws, the second changing the direction of play. After three hits the successful one claims one durb as his prize. If players are not using the same type of durb there is usually an agreement – three for a roocher, four for a glassack, and six for a steelack. Pronts were at a disadvantage. They were bigger targets.

Punkie

Ideally not more than four to play. A hole is made in the ground 4-5 inches wide and 3 inches deep. Players stand back 12 feet and throw in rotation to the hole. Competitor nearest the hole throws for the hole again, and, if successful, to hit an adversary durb. If he hits he scores one. He is then allowed to throw for the punky hole again. If successful repeats process of hitting an adversary. If not, next nearest throws for the punky, and so on.

Knocking Out Of The Ring

Up to four play. A ring of 12" diameter is marked on the ground. Each contributes two or three marbles which are placed in the ring. Players throw in rotation from 12 feet to hit durbs in the ring. Any durbs knocked out of the ring are won.

Hen In The Bush

This was a real gambler's game. You put some or no marbles in one hand and cover it with the other. Opponent guesses number of marbles held. If right, he takes all. If wrong he contributes the difference between his guess and number held.

CATTIE

Up to four play. The cattie is a piece of wood four inches long and squared to one inch on all sides. Each side has a number 1 – 4. The ends of the wood are pointed. A shallow hole 3" in diameter is made in the ground and the cattie placed across it. The first player, using a stick 2'6" long inserts it under the cattie to flick it forward. If cattie caught in flight – out. If not

168

read number uppermost on the cattie – say 3. First player then strikes point of cattie to make it jump and tries to hit it in the air. This three times and competitors can catch in the air to stop innings. If first player gets by unscathed, then stick lengths between final resting place of cattie and the hole is the score.

STOOKO MANNIES

Up to six to play. Players stand in a line, with "It" in front facing. "It" takes each by the wrist and pulls forward sharply. Each on being pulled adopts a funny attitude and holds it like a statue. "It" then chooses the funniest and exchanges places.

RELIEVER

Any number in two teams. Teams could be chosen by "Eese ose, man's brose, eese ose out," or "Eetle ottle, black bottle, ettle ottle out." Or with all holding arms bent at the elbows and fists clenched, with the patter as each fist is touched, "One potato, two potato, three potato, four, five potato, six potato, seven potato, more." The fist struck on "more," goes down. When two fists are down, they are of the chosen.

A den is determined – like a length of fence. The out team goes off to rove or to hide. Then there is an option. The "ins" count to 100 or await the call from the "outs" of "reliever." The "ins" then go in pursuit. An "out" is captured with three pats on the head and becomes a prisoner in the den. He can be released by an "out" crashing the den without being caught, and shouting "reliever." A phase is finished when all the "outs" are captured and are in the den – if ever. The streets of Inverness were perhaps never alive with the sounds of music, but they certainly were with the cry of RELIEVER.

GURDS

Politely known as a hoop, a gurd could be a posh job from a Blacksmith or the Sporting Stores, or more likely a bicycle wheel rim, or a motor bike or car tyre. The gurd was pro-

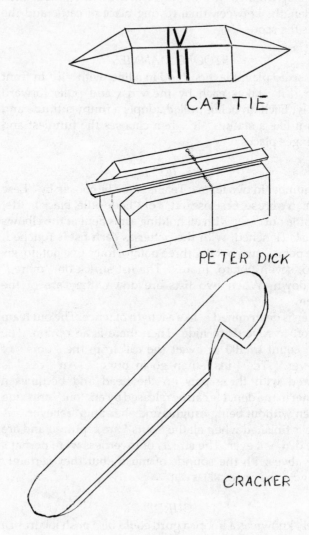

CAT TIE

PETER DICK

CRACKER

pelled and guided with a small stick, and was used for racing – straight or obstacle races.

SKEETCHIE

This is better known as Hop Scotch, and calls for no explanation.

CIGARETTE CARDS

Two to four players. Cigarette cards were provided with most brands of cigarettes, and were easily come by as most adults seemed to smoke. They came in series such as Famous Footballers, Famous People, Birds, Ships, Flowers. On one side was a picture, on the reverse a short text descriptive of the picture. Each side had a frame, a line about an eighth of an inch from the edge. The game was played against a wall from which players stood back 12'. The first player took a card between the first and middle fingers and flicked it towards the wall. The others followed suit. The player overlapping a card to the extent of the frame took all cards on the ground.

PETER DICK

See the sketch. The Peter could be rattled from the small finger to the index finger, and the conventional tune was – ''Peter Dick, Peter Dick, Peter Dick, Dick, Dick.''

CRACKERS

See the sketch. The crackers were held between the first and middle, and the middle and fourth fingers. The cracker between the first and middle was held stationary by the thumb, and the arm shaken to make the other crack upon it.

"Fag Cairds"

GLOSSARY

spurtle, round stick 12″ long, ½″ thick for stirring porridge.

softies, soft biscuits of the morning roll type.

klaik, to tattle.

scud, a run, as on a scooter, bike, cart, or such like.

speldeens, smoked haddock.

bowsher, errand boy.

hotching, teeming.

sonsie, buxom, fat.

skelped, slapped.

gadgie, small boy, urchin.

dalacher round the lug, clip round the ear.

crowdie, cottage cheese, made with sour milk.

punkie(y), marbles game.

durb, marble.

rooched, won in a game of marbles.

glassacks, glass marbles.

Peter Dick, small wooden rattle played with fingers of one hand.

crackers, flat sticks held between the fingers and flicked.

hurley, wheel-barrow.

parrs, small fish, tiddlers.

ribwort, narrow leaved plantain, ribgrass.

skeetch, to skim stones on water.

stots, bounces.

crust, head.

bogie roll, black twist tobacco.

tiles, tile hats.

pieces, slices of bread, buttered or jammed, or both.

headacks, heading a ball.
keep uppity, keeping the ball in the air with foot flicks.
durl, painful feeling.
harled, coated in a mixture of lime and aggregates.
groick, awkward, clumsy person.
airt, direction, or quarter.
Lochgelly, leather strap used for punishment in school.
dossan, hair cut short, with a small tuft left in front.
hoch, cheap cut of beef.
pan drops, boiled sweets.
rosebuds, boiled sweets.
boiling, in this case also boiled sweets.
but and ben, two roomed cottage.
couthy, good natured.
dottle, remains of tobacco left in a pipe after smoking.
cailleach, old woman.
mutch, woman's cap.
k'yarack, left hand.
semmit, singlet.
tred, trade.
blethers, garrulous folk.
oxter, armpit.
stotting, bouncing.
clype (to), to tell tales out of school.
mergansers, fish eating, spike billed ducks.
kyolls, newly born birds.
spangs, steps or paces.

INDEX
OF
NON-FICTIONAL NAMES
MENTIONED IN THE TEXT